CONTENTS

The BBC presents the 103rd Season of Henry Wood Promenade Concerts

Royal Albert Hall

18 July to 13 September 1997

Published by:
BBC Radio 3 Publications.
Editorial Office: Room 815,
Henry Wood House,
3-6 Langham Place,
London W1A 1AA.

Distributed by BBC Books, a
division of BBC Worldwide,
80 Wood Lane,
London W12 0TT

© BBC 1997
ISBN 0 563 383798
Design: Ideology, London
Cover Illustration:
Jeff Fisher at CIA, London
Advertising: Hugh Muirhead
Printed by Taylor Bloxham
Limited, Leicester

Don't miss your free CD in back cover!

Introduction

THE PROMS ARE FOR EVERYONE. At a time when media myth has it that some audiences find the formality of concerts off-putting and the demands of classical music difficult, the Proms annually prove otherwise. The Proms are where quality and popularity meet in an ideal balance, where there are absolutely no demands other than the will to concentrate on great music.

Last year, we introduced the idea of not a single theme but a mosaic-like pattern of small themes, linked and threaded through the season.

This year we develop that, with a rich vein of anniversary celebrations, two major featured composers of this century, and a look at the fascinating and varied influence of folk music on the classical repertory.

We hope we have found some unusual ways of marking this year's anniversaries: Brahms we explore not only as a towering composer, with his symphonies and rarer choral works, but also as a leading conductor of his time and a pioneering student of early music. We will explore the music that Brahms loved and himself conducted, from Beethoven's *Missa Solemnis*, to works from Schütz and Bach to Berlioz and Mendelssohn.

Schubert's bicentenary is marked with several of his symphonies, of course, but also with a serene Mass and a very rare hearing of a lyrical one-act opera that is the most successful drama he set. The music of Mendelssohn, 150 years after his death, is featured by the Leipzig Gewandhaus Orchestra which he conducted, who bring programmes entirely of music they have premiered through their history, from Brahms in the nineteenth century to Hans Werner Henze, new last year.

Nearer to our own time, we revive two works by the extraordinary prodigy Erich Wolfgang Korngold, born 100 years ago (Henry Wood introduced the music of this fifteen-year-old to the Proms in 1912, and he must surely still be the youngest Proms composer ever) and there is a fiftieth-birthday concert for (and conducted by) John Adams.

Two twentieth-century composers receive special attention, following last year's major Stravinsky series. Bartók's music has elemental power and roots in folk culture which makes him a perfect composer to speak for our times. I'm especially pleased that the leading international visiting orchestras this season are all bringing important works by Bartók.

The second featured composer of our century is Britten, whose supremely humane music will resound through a wide-ranging weekend with concerts, a late-night church parable, and a lecture by Philip Brett, culminating in the BBC Symphony Orchestra's *War Requiem* under Andrew Davis. We will be welcoming the International Musicological Congress to London at this time, marked by two showcase late-night concerts of British music old and new.

Below
A scene from the premiere production of Henze's *Venus and Adonis,* at the Bavarian State Opera, Munich, January 1997

Above right
Two of the world's leading composers at the Proms: Elliott Carter, receiving the Royal Philharmonic Society Gold Medal from Sir Michael Tippett, at the first Proms Chamber Music Concert last year. Their music is heard this season in Proms 27 and 51

Director

*Nicholas Kenyon, Controller,
BBC Radio 3*

Assistant

Yvette Pusey

Administrator

Stephen Maddock

Secretary

Ceri Hunter

Marketing Manager

Judy Grahame

Publicity Officer

Leonora Thomson

Secretaries

*Eve Saunders and
Judith Jerome*

**Senior Producer,
BBC Radio 3**

Edward Blakeman

Publications Editor

George Hall

Publications Organiser

Karen Cardy

Assistant Editor

Edward Bhesania

Publications Officer

Sarah Breeden

Secretary

Liesl Burger

Leading the way as ever in new music, the Proms present works new to this country, including Elliott Carter's latest orchestral work, and works by John Adams, the late Tristan Keuris and the eighty-year-old Lou Harrison. We are particularly fortunate to have secured at the last stage of our planning the British premiere of Henze's highly praised new opera *Venus and Adonis*. The BBC Symphony Orchestra plays new commissions by two leading reinventors of the orchestra, Iannis Xenakis in his seventy-fifth year and the American Roger Reynolds.

The BBC Philharmonic brings the first in a series of new works by Peter Maxwell Davies, and Jonathan Harvey's new concerto for Evelyn Glennie; the BBC National Orchestra of Wales a new piece by David Sawer; the BBC Scottish Symphony an Edward McGuire work featuring bagpipes and a newly-rediscovered tone-poem by Sibelius.

Composers whose music is heard for the first time in the Proms range from the sixteenth-century John Sheppard to contemporaries Giya Kancheli, Stephen Montague, Frank Zappa and one of the best songwriting partnerships ever, Lennon and McCartney. (For those who believe that honour belongs to Gilbert and Sullivan, they are there too, with a complete *Gondoliers!*)

Threaded through the concerts are all sorts of folk-influenced pieces from Luciano Berio's settings of Folk Songs and the nationalist folk tunes in Glinka and Rimsky-Korsakov to Beethoven's remarkably literal birdsongs in his 'Pastoral' Symphony and Haydn's witty use of the hornsignal. Mahler quoting *Frère Jacques*, Percy Grainger using non-Western sources in *The Warriors*, Colin McPhee inspiring Britten by using gamelan music, and composers as diverse as Chopin, Liszt, Shostakovich and Sibelius drawing more loosely on traditional sources, all show the power of folk music. And for the genuine article we have invited the famous Rustavi Choir to give their own piercingly authentic accounts of Georgian folk songs.

A special feature of our casting this year, when the BBC celebrates its vital contribution to the creation and nurturing of talent at the time of its seventy-fifth anniversary, is to present some musical prize-winners who first came to wide attention in BBC broadcasts and have gone on to make major careers: singers Karita Mattila, Inger Dam-Jensen and Bryn Terfel, and instrumentalists Natalie Clein, Nicholas Daniel and Ilya Itin.

The late-night concerts offer the greatest variety and some leading popular artists: Joanna MacGregor, the King's Singers and Sir Simon Rattle. Among our major innovations last year, both the Junior Prom especially conceived for school-children and the Proms in the Park on the Last Night both clearly made a mark, and return this year.

The complementary Proms Chamber Music series, which expands and reflects the themes of our programmes, continues every Monday lunchtime, this time at the Victoria & Albert Museum. Make a day of your visit to the Proms and explore the season's music to the full.

On BBC Radio 3, where every one of the Proms is broadcast live, there will be more links than ever with the season: Proms Artists of the Week and Composers of the Week and, for the first time, regular repeats of Proms broadcasts on weekday afternoons. Each summer the Proms sum up everything that Radio 3 stands for through the rest of the year: together, they represent a unique investment in our cultural life. Enjoy them both.

Nicholas Kenyon

Nicholas Kenyon
Controller, BBC Radio 3

BBC Singe

Stephen Cleobury *Chief Conductor*

"*The BBC Singers
are arguably our
finest professional
choir*" Richard Morrison, The Times

Catering to music tastes from...

A

Acid · African/South African · Ambient · Arabic · Ballads

Big Band · Bluegrass · Blues · Brass Band · Cajun/Creole

Cantonese · Caribbean · ChaCha · Children's · C...

Christian Contemporary · Christian Trad...

Compilations/TV · Country · Dance · D...

Listening/MOR · Film · Soundtracks · Fla...

to

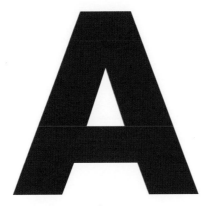

Flamenco · Foll... Gaelic · Glam Rock · Gospel · Grunge

Heavy Meta... Metal · Hip Hop · Hokkin House · Indian

Industri... ...le · Klezmer · Latino · Latin Rock · Malay

Ma... ...Mucho · Musical Theatre · New Age · Opera

Z

Orchestral · Paso Doble · Perfor... ...illy · Punk

Raggamuffin · Rap · Reggae · R... ...a · Samba

Schlager · Ska · Soul · Spok... ...W... ...Traditional

World Beat · Zulu

EMI GROUP PLC 4 TENTERDEN STREET HANOVER SQUARE LONDON W1A 2AY
TELEPHONE 0171-355 4848 FAX 0171-495 1308

'I TAKE PLEASURE in attacking the folklorists, who try to apply to the ideas of popular music, which are by nature primitive, a technique which is only appropriate to a more evolved type of thought.' Thus Arnold Schoenberg, on typically caustic form, writing in 1925. Whatever the reasons behind Schoenberg's polemic, it is widely felt that the conjunction of so-called centuries is on offer, ranging from Beethoven's affectionate cameo of peasant dancing in the 'Pastoral' Symphony through Dvořák's allusion to Czech dance in his Eighth Symphony to Luciano Berio's quirky resetting of a variety of exotic originals in his *Folk Songs*. By the end of the season it will hopefully be clear that when composers draw inspiration from a traditional culture, they need not be indulging in pseudo-folkloristic sentimentality – 'fakesong' as one commentator termed it. In fact, it is difficult to

Folk into Art

Julian Anderson teases out the strands of folk culture running through the 1997 season

Above
Percy Grainger
recording Danish folk
songs in 1925

folk or traditional cultures with Western 'art' music has been fraught with difficulties, not least in the present century. The grim tenets of socialist realism – 'music for the people' – and the innumerable, unbearably cliché-ridden folk oratorios and operas which it produced, have severely discredited the whole business of composers exploring folk traditions.

This year's Proms should go some way to correcting the picture. A rich selection of folk-inspired concert music from the last two

predict what music might result as the encounter can take on different, even contradictory forms.

Take the case of Percy Grainger, whose polyorchestral jamboree *The Warriors* is heard in Prom 9. Australian-born, this staunchly individualistic composer was obsessive about all folk cultures, especially if they happened to be Nordic (by which he meant both British and Scandinavian). Although probably the most scientific of the British folk song collectors, his reflection of traditional music in

The Warriors is more generalised, less literal than that of Vaughan Williams or Butterworth. Triggered by a suggestion from Sir Thomas Beecham that Grainger try his hand at ballet, this is an extravagant twenty-minute tone-poem for huge and strangely constituted orchestra – including several offstage bands, multiple pianos, harps and 'tuneful percussion', requiring three conductors to co-ordinate its benign chaos. Grainger concocted elaborate 'mind-pictures' to stimulate his imagination, a bizarre pot-pourri of warriors from every tribe he could think of, including ancient Greeks, Zulus, Vikings, Polynesians, Amazonians and native Americans, 'all arm-in-arm in a united show of gay and innocent pride, fierce and exultant'. Those last three words certainly describe the resultant music perfectly: the revival of this complex, rarely heard work is not to be missed.

Composers often draw inspiration from traditional poetry rather than its music. Mahler's many settings of poems from the traditional anthology *Des Knaben Wunderhorn* are typical of this; several were subsequently incorporated into his earlier symphonies. Similarly, Shostakovich's song-cycle *From Jewish Folk Poetry*, in which the composer sets traditional texts to original music, does not quote any folk themes, but the composer imbued his melodic style with intonations redolent of Jewish melodies –

notably those obsessively drooping minor thirds. The music is also saturated with a bitter-sweet ironical tone which Shostakovich saw as typical of Jewish music, and which in turn was to become deeply characteristic of his own.

Alternatively, a set of folk tales may serve as the pretext for elaborate and colourful orchestral invention, as in Rimsky-Korsakov's *Sheherazade*, inspired by the Arabian *Tales of 1001 Nights*. But most of Sibelius's non-symphonic orchestral music, such as *Luonnotar* and the recently rediscovered *The Wood Nymph*, is similarly a retelling of traditional stories, as is his massive *Kullervo Symphony*.

Sibelius's chief source of inspiration was the *Kalevala*, a lengthy Finnish saga taken down from oral traditions and published as literature in the mid-nineteenth century (probably not without some distortion of the originals). No strict attempts to ape folk music here – more a wish to render in vivid sound-pictures the fantastical events of the narrative. Sibelius the mature symphonist, also heard plentifully this season, came to have serious reservations about the early *Kullervo*, perhaps feeling its pictorialism to be too literal. But the rough-hewn, startling sonorities of many passages provide the earliest glimpse of his highly original orchestral palette, and some parts even seem to presage his late masterpiece *Tapiola*.

The direct quotation of folk song

is the simplest way to incorporate some aspect of traditional music – but also, as already mentioned, the most naive and potentially risky. The Russian 'Group of Five' (Rimsky-Korsakov, Musorgsky, Balakirev, Borodin and Cui) were all fond of quoting folk songs. Such allusions were not the exclusive province of the Five: Tchaikovsky was not a member of the group, but he too had a go at 'concertising' folk music in several works, including the ever popular First Piano Concerto.

This approach reaches its zenith with the early Stravinsky ballets, all three of which will be heard this season. Premiered in Paris by the Dyagilev troupe, these immediately established Stravinsky's reputation in the West as a leading modernist composer. But as the scholar Richard Taruskin has recently shown in his huge study of Stravinsky's early compositions, allusions to folk material were already considered *passé* amongst progressive Russian composers by this time, even if the increasing dissonance and polyrhythms in which Stravinsky clothed his chosen tunes caused growing surprise, not least in *The Rite of Spring*.

The second of the three ballets, *Petrushka*, neatly illustrates the financial dangers of borrowing apparently traditional tunes. To portray the organ grinder at his Shrovetide fair, Stravinsky quoted a simple melody he had transcribed from a French street musician; the

Top
George Benjamin
Bottom
Nikolay Rimsky-Korsakov

Right
Britten and Colin
McPhee (seated) on
Long Island, c1940
Bottom right
Bartók, 1934

melody ('He had a Wooden Leg') turned out to be in copyright, a fact which has cost Stravinsky's publishers an exorbitant ten per cent of the royalties ever since!

Other composers have tended to be more oblique in their approach. Bartók, whose music features prominently this season, put the matter well when he commented that ideally a composer should simply 'soak himself' in folk music to the point where its idioms became so natural that even the composer is unsure whether he is alluding to it or not. Then, too, many twentieth-century composers since Debussy have felt the pull towards more distant traditional musics, such as those of Indonesia or Japan, in an effort to renew their whole aesthetic.

Britten's affection for the complex metallic orchestras of the

Balinese gamelan is well known. Less well known is his initial source of information about such music, the Canadian composer Colin McPhee, whom Britten met in New York in the early 1940s. McPhee's obsession with the gamelan was such that he actually lived in Bali for several years to study it. *Tabuh-tabuhan* is his largest piece reflecting that experience, a vividly orchestrated three-movement work incorporating an appropriately prominent tuned percussion band.

Asian or Oriental musics lie behind a number of contemporary items this season. The bright sonorities of Steve Reich's *Music for Mallet Instruments, Voices and Organ* are perhaps gamelan-inspired, although the composer is quick to condemn 'the old exoticism approach' of many Western composers, and insists that

it is the structure, not the sound, of such music that interests him. The drifting string harmonics of the third of George Benjamin's *Three Inventions* were suggested by the floating pentatonic chords of the traditional Japanese mouth organ, the *shō*. Both Indonesian and Japanese music have also proved lasting influences in the music of the American composer Lou Harrison.

In the best of these works the aim is not to patronise or to copy a traditional music. Rather, composers discover through their encounter with traditions, whether of the West or the East, something fundamental about themselves, perhaps even about music itself. The results are not a cultural dilution, but at best refresh the sometimes slightly claustrophobic world of art music with something more immediate, uninhibited and, yes, complicated. Perhaps even Schoenberg would have been pleased.

Try this simple form of meditation.

Focus on this dot.

Stare into it for a few moments.

See it as a door.

An opening.

A vessel into which

your mind is flowing.

Once inside,

your heartbeat

begins to slow.

You feel peaceful.

Calm.

Serene.

You'll feel the same

opening the door of an E-class Mercedes.

Mercedes-Benz

Schubert

Elizabeth Norman McKay finds neglected
riches among Schubert's music

the unknown

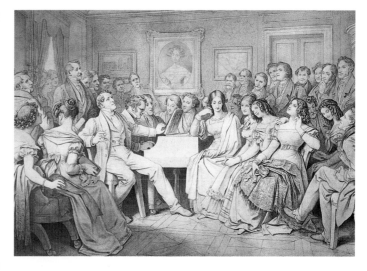

FRANZ SCHUBERT was born on 31 January 1797 in one of the poorer suburbs of Vienna, the son of a hard-pressed elementary school-teacher. Contrary to popular opinion, when he died in November 1828 at the age of thirty-one, he was neither destitute nor an obscure, unrecognised composer, but a well-known and respected figure in Viennese musical circles. In the preceding eight years he had seen nearly 200 of his songs and part-songs published, together with a large quantity of works for solo piano – mostly collections of short popular dances, but also the 'Wanderer' Fantasy and three sonatas – and virtually all of his later piano duets. In addition, several of his chamber works had been performed.

But all these compositions were destined for domestic settings and salons, or other small venues. This was not what Schubert had in mind when, early in 1813, after being overwhelmed by a performance of a Gluck work at the Court Opera, he made the ultimate decision 'to dedicate his life to Art'. As he well knew, to succeed as a serious composer he would have to make his mark not in the world of small-scale private music-making but in the grander public arena, with music for the theatre, large sacred choral works, and symphonies for the concert hall. But Schubert did not live long enough to succeed, and to this day whole swathes of his public music, notably his works for the theatre, remain virtually unknown.

Early in 1817, soon after his twentieth birthday, Schubert was introduced to the illustrious opera singer Johann Michael Vogl, the leading baritone at the Court Opera. Vogl took Schubert under his wing, becoming his patron and adviser. At the end of 1818 he won for Schubert his first theatrical commission: to write for the court theatre a one-act farce of the kind then popular. For Schubert this was his first big break into the professional musical world and for the next few years his future in the theatre looked promising. In 1820 and 1821 three of his works were staged in Vienna, and he was invited to compose a further German opera.

Left, main picture
Vienna, around 1820
Left inset
Portrait of Schubert by Gábor Melegh
Above
A Schubert evening at Baron von Spaun's: Johann Michael Vogl turns pages at the piano

But the palmy days of a booming operatic scene in Vienna were coming to an end. The strict censorship laws imposed by the Austrian state to preserve peace and order were encouraging a taste for ephemeral, escapist entertainment at the expense of new serious German operas. In 1822 Schubert submitted two full-length German Romantic operas and a one-act Singspiel to the Court theatre, none of which was accepted. The Singspiel, a charming, effervescent little work, was *Die Verschworenen* ('The Conspirators'), renamed *Der häusliche Krieg* ('Domestic Warfare') by the ever-zealous censors in their determination to prevent political unrest. In the opera, based on Aristophanes' comedy *Lysistrata*, the wives of Crusader-knights go on a sexual strike until their husbands forswear war. The Singspiel became immensely popular after its first concert performance, conducted by the great Schubert enthusiast Johann Herbeck, in Vienna early in 1861, and within a few months it was in the repertory of the Court Opera. When six years later George Grove and Arthur Sullivan arrived in Vienna in search of unfamiliar music by Schubert, Herbeck surely pointed them towards *Die Verschworenen*. In some of the comic operas which Sullivan wrote later in the century, the sounds and spirit of the music of Schubert's Singspiel were surely ringing in his ears.

By the time Schubert completed *Fierrabras* in the autumn of 1823, Viennese audiences had succumbed to the delights of Rossini. The Court Opera had an Italian director, and the company consisted almost entirely of Italian singers (Vogl was one of the German-speaking singers who had been pensioned off or dismissed) able to satisfy a veritable craze for Rossini's operas. When the craze subsided a few years later, there were neither audiences nor performers to maintain the theatre. In dire financial straits, it was forced to close its doors for months on end; indeed, for the last four or five years of Schubert's life, virtually no new German operas were produced at the Court theatre, nor at the Theater an der Wien, which was also in financial trouble. Schubert was not without theatrical talent, but as a composer of German opera he could scarcely have lived at a worse time.

Schubert composed some forty sacred works, several of which were published in his lifetime, while others circulated in manuscript copies. Most of them were written for specific occasions and for churches with which he had connections.

The outstanding exception was the Missa Solemnis in A flat, one of his greatest and most personal compositions. He began it in 1819 with the ambitious intention of dedicating it either to the Emperor or Empress, returned to it in 1822, and finally revised it in late 1825 or early 1826, thus giving more attention to it over a longer period than to

almost any other of his compositions. In February 1828 he offered it for publication to Schott in Mainz, claiming in an accompanying letter that here was proof of his 'striving toward the highest peaks in art'.

In Schubert's sacred music, although he could never bring himself to proclaim a belief in 'one holy catholic and apostolic church', words which he simply deleted in his Mass settings, mention of the Virgin Mary always seemed to awaken a special quality in his music. In the Credo of this Mass, the inspiration of the slow 'Et incarnatus est' is breathtaking. In the powerful Sanctus, angel choirs seem to voice the cries of 'Holy! Holy! Holy!', while the glories of 'heaven and earth' are buoyed up by the heavenly orchestral breezes that separate them. This is stirring music indeed.

Despite Schubert's 1825–6 amendments to his score to lessen the strains on performers, the Mass still makes considerable demands on singers and instrumentalists. For this reason it was probably never performed in his lifetime. Even more surprisingly, this great work was not published until 1875, and even then in the 1822 version. Schubert's final version, one of the highest peaks amongst his masterpieces, had to wait until 1887.

Schubert was composing symphonies and overtures from an early age. Each of his first six symphonies (of 1813–18) was performed by an amateur orchestra, the first two by the student orchestra of the Stadtkonvikt where he boarded during his schooldays in Vienna. The other four were played by an orchestral society which had grown from a small chamber music group meeting in the Schuberts' school-house and, as numbers grew, later transferred to larger premises in the city. By 1817 it was a proficient orchestra, attracting some of the finest local amateur players, some professionals, and a small audience. (Schubert played viola, and his brother Ferdinand first violin.)

Of the few professional concerts with orchestra given in Vienna at this time, most were either charity events or benefit concerts for instrumental soloists, who performed concertos and showpieces displaying their particular talents to best advantage. Schubert was no virtuoso pianist or violinist. He could neither perform such music, nor did he show much inclination to write it. (The only concerto attributed to him, for violin, is probably by his

brother Ferdinand.) A complete symphony in a concert was thus a rarity, a single movement more usual. Overtures by Schubert occasionally appeared in these programmes, but they served as appetisers at the start of either half. Thus Schubert had little opportunity to break through as a composer for the professional concert hall.

There were, however, two prestigious amateur musical organisations in Vienna that arranged concerts which, although ostensibly private, attracted good audiences – those of the Musikverein (Society of Friends of Music) and the Concerts Spirituels – both of which made a point of including pieces from the symphonic repertoire in their programmes. When he composed his 'Great' C major Symphony, Schubert had in mind the larger concerts (four each year) of the Musikverein in the Great Hall of the Imperial Palace. Shortly after his death the Society opened its concert with one of Schubert's symphonies – not the 'Great' C major, which was deemed too long and too difficult to perform, but the Symphony No. 6, also in C major. This was the first appearance of any of Schubert's symphonies in a major concert in Vienna, and he missed the occasion by just five weeks. He had, however, known that it was to be played. His future looked more promising, and he was already working on a new symphony. Had he lived longer, who knows what success might have been his?

A World of Music

Founded on the great European traditions of instrument making and music publishing, the Boosey & Hawkes Group is today one of the world's foremost music companies.

Our international roster of twentieth-century composers is unrivalled and our instruments and accessories are used by performers throughout the world. In both advanced and developing countries we are exercising an important influence, as more people turn to music as a popular leisure pursuit.

In the field of music education, we are firmly committed to developing future generations of musicians by providing them with access to instruments and printed music of the highest quality.

From school concerts to the Proms, from bandrooms to opera houses, on radio and television, Boosey & Hawkes helps the world to enjoy the gift of music.

BOOSEY & HAWKES

Photography credits: SBC/Richard Haughton (Lindberg), Elektra/Nonesuch (Reich), Hanya Chlala (Maxwell Davies), Misha Donat (Carter), Nonesuch/Deborah Feingold (Adams).

Magnus Lindberg

Benjamin Britten

Steve Reich

Sir Peter Maxwell Davies

Elliott Carter

John Adams

Serge Rachmaninoff

Bally.
What a
feeling.

On all of life's big
occasions, Bally
Scribe shoes give
you exclusive status.
With genuine welts
for maximum comfort
and durability.
Bally's tradition and
experience guarantee
impeccable quality
with style.

BALLY
S W I T Z E R L A N D

SINCE 1851

D·R·O·O·P·Y· & B·R·O·W·N·S· BY ANGELA HOLMES

Photograph: Anthony Crickmay   Instrument by Shem Mackey, Viol and Violin Maker – 0171 729 5225

ROBERT SCHUMANN CALLED him 'the Mozart of the nineteenth century', and for many of his contemporaries Felix Mendelssohn did indeed have all Mozart's gifts, first as a child prodigy, then as a mature composer and performer, a man and artist who summed up the best qualities of his age.

His finest music has a freshness and directness of expression that place him among the greatest composers, but in the century following his death his reputation suffered badly, and often unjustly.

with Wagner's personal views of musical progress; and perhaps there is also a hint of the anti-semitism that eventually led to Mendelssohn's music being entirely suppressed under the Third Reich.

Even where he was most valued, it was often for his weaker aspects, such as the streak of sentimental piety that so appealed to Victorian English audiences (including, of course, Queen Victoria herself). This aspect was reinforced by the heavier performing style of the later nineteenth century, which thickened his instrumental textures and tended to weaken the rhythmic impulse of much of his music. (Anyone who has ever spent childhood piano lessons

A frightening talent

Andrew Huth explores the genius of Mendelssohn, who died 150 years ago

His more adventurous contemporaries – Berlioz, Glinka, Chopin, Schumann, Liszt, Wagner – provided a greater inspiration to the future, while Mendelssohn often served as the figurehead of timid conservatives. Wagner even saw him as a tragic figure; 'such an enormous talent as Mendelssohn's is frightening, it has no place in the development of our music. A landscape painter, incapable of depicting a human being'. Mendelssohn clearly didn't fit in

murdering a *Song Without Words* knows how easy it is to play Mendelssohn badly.)

There is even something unsatisfactory about his blameless personal life. Wouldn't he be more highly regarded as a composer if his biography featured drink, drugs, debt, adultery, secret vices, madness? Or if he had struggled in a garret and died in obscure poverty?

As it was, his development as a musical Wunderkind was stimulated by an exceptionally happy and

privileged background. The Mendelssohn family home in Berlin was a lively intellectual centre with regular concerts, theatrical performances and literary readings.

Felix would have excelled in whatever profession he chose: his wide and thorough education covered classics, science, languages and law, among several other subjects, and until he was sixteen it was by no means taken for granted that he would become a musician.

But music had to predominate in the end. From the age of eleven he composed fluently and prolifically. His first publication, a piano quartet, appeared in 1823, when he was just fourteen. A mass of piano and chamber music, five concertos, a few little operas and twelve symphonies for strings preceded his official Symphony No. 1 of 1824. Then came the works which demonstrated not just skill but real depth and maturity: chief among them the Octet for strings (1825) and a year later the overture to *A Midsummer Night's Dream*. In his early twenties he travelled around Europe, beginning in 1829 with the first of his many visits to England. In the course of his journeys he met everyone worth meeting and heard everyone worth hearing. His letters home show his alert, intelligent reactions to whatever he encountered, and also his firmly-held artistic and social opinions. His sensitivity to the spirit of the places he visited can be heard in such works as the 'Italian' and 'Scottish' symphonies and the *Hebrides* Overture.

Mendelssohn was aware of living at a time of great cultural and

political change. As the grandson of an eminent Jewish philosopher and son of a wealthy banker, he was very conscious of what his own family had gained from the civil rights and social emancipation which Jews had recently acquired in the post-Napoleonic period. When Abraham Mendelssohn had his four children baptised in 1816 (the future composer was seven years old) he was not trying to deny their religious or racial background, but wanted to place it in the context of a self-consciously German, thoroughly modern Enlightenment culture.

In both music and life, Mendelssohn accepted and welcomed this culture. Musically, it meant the unbroken tradition of German music deriving from Bach, who was always his musical ideal; and Bach, Handel, the Viennese classics (including the still little-known late works of Beethoven and Schubert) were the standard against which he composed. He never wanted to reproduce the past, but in each of his major works searched for new approaches to Classical formal

problems. He was rarely satisfied with his own facility. He often kept major scores for a long time before presenting them to the public, and then revised them thoroughly after performance. The 'Scottish' Symphony, conceived during his first visit to Britain in 1829, did not reach performance until twelve years later. The 'Italian' Symphony was begun in 1831 and first performed in London in 1834, but Mendelssohn could never make up his mind about some of the details, so the score was not published during his lifetime. The Violin Concerto occupied him for over six years and he pondered over *Elijah* for nearly eight.

Even if he had never composed a note himself, Mendelssohn would still be a great figure in the history of music for his work as a pianist, organist, conductor, organiser and advocate of other composers' music, both old and new. His dedication to the revival of Bach's music is well known, beginning with his 1829 performances of the *St Matthew Passion*, the first since Bach's lifetime. But just as important were his efforts on behalf of Handel, Mozart and Beethoven. As conductor of the Leipzig Gewandhaus Orchestra from 1835 and then founder of the Leipzig Conservatory in 1843 he insisted on – and usually achieved – the highest standards in every field. He was tireless and generous in promoting the music of his contemporaries, even if he didn't personally like it. Although the

Far left The living room of Mendelssohn's home in Leipzig in a watercolour by the composer
Top Mendelssohn's wife, Cecile
Bottom Mendelssohn's sister, the composer Fanny Hensel

'disorder' of Berlioz's music horrified him, he did all he could to make the French composer's 1843 Leipzig visit a success. Berlioz was duly grateful, but wickedly imagined the citizens of Leipzig piously intoning, 'There is no God but Bach, and Mendelssohn is his prophet'.

There is one sad gap in the long list of Mendelssohn's works – a mature opera. He seriously considered a number of subjects, among them Shakespeare's *Tempest* and the Nibelungen legends, but nothing ever came of these plans. He did, however, write a great deal of incidental music for the theatre. And among his best overtures is *Ruy Blas*, composed at great speed in 1839 for a performance of Victor Hugo's swashbuckling play.

There is plenty of drama in the oratorios, and particularly in the cantata *Die erste Walpurgisnacht*, a setting of Goethe's poem which describes Druids preparing to observe their ancient hilltop pagan rituals. From fear of persecution by their Christian conquerors they create a diversion by placing at the foot of the hill a group of watchers who create a hideous, satanic din to frighten off any strangers who come too close. On this last visit to Goethe in 1830, Mendelssohn discussed his intention of setting this strange poem. The old poet explained that 'it must repeatedly happen in the course of world history that something old, established, tested and reassuring is probed, harassed and oppressed by the emergence of new ideas'.

Mendelssohn was highly sensitive to the opposing claims of the 'old, established, tested and reassuring' and 'the emergence of new ideas', and achieved his greatest successes by finding elegant solutions to the problem that faces all composers in all ages: a perfect balance between old and new. After calling him 'the Mozart of the nineteenth century', Robert Schumann went on to admire him as 'the most illuminating of musicians, who sees more clearly than others through the contradictions of our era and is the first to reconcile them'.

Mendelssohn's music can be heard in Proms 5, 37, 42 (Die erste Walpurgisnacht), 52, 53, 54, 62 and 69

Above
A seventeenth-century representation of a Walpurgisnacht
Top left
Sir Neville Marriner conducts the Violin Concerto and 'Scottish' Symphony with the Leipzig Gewandhaus Orchestra in Proms 52 and 53
Bottom left
Mark Elder conducts *Die erste Walpurgisnacht* in Prom 42

Modern Classics

"Whoever made these cables clearly loves the job..."

HiFi Choice

Audio Interconnect Cables
Home Theatre Interconnect Cables
Speaker Cables
Bullion Series Plugs
Audio Control & Switching Units
Deadrock Equipment Supports
Sound Enhancement Products

IXOS

the collection

For more details and a colour brochure detailing these and many more innovative and award winning products please call

01494 441736

One of life's more rewarding decisions.

KEF Reference Series

If only all decisions in life were as straightforward as this. The fact is that if you want the purest sound and the most uncompromising specification, it simply has to be New KEF Reference.

Every speaker must match our engineers' 'reference' prototype to an almost unbelievable tolerance of 0.5 decibels. This means you can be sure that the sound originally achieved at KEF will be recreated in your home. Exactly.

Our breakthrough Uni-Q® technology delivers an astonishing stereo image, its unique point source design, with the tweeter at the exact acoustic centre of the mid-range cone, lets you visualise the precise location of every performer on the stage. What's more, because of Uni-Q's smooth,

even dispersion you'll hear that incredible realism throughout the room. From speakers this good you'd expect outstanding bass performance. With KEF's famous 'coupled cavity' bass system, now further improved with interports, you get it. We go to similar extremes in perfecting every detail. Some you can't see, like Oxygen-Free Copper internal wiring or magnetic shielding (vital in Home Theatre). Some you can - sumptuously veneered cabinets with heavily gold-plated feet and terminals, for example.

In other words, each pair of Reference speakers is as close to perfection as KEF can make it.

When you know you can choose the best, would you willingly settle for anything less?

KEF

The experience of sound

Brahms
the performer, editor and collector

Leon Botstein looks at some little-known aspects of Brahms's creativity

Left
Print after a painting by
Willy von Beckerath

Centre
Brahms conducting, by
Willy von Beckerath

A PERSISTENT and nagging sense of cultural decline was discernible among composers of the generation of Mendelssohn and Schumann. More than one observer born after 1800 suspected that, in the world of music, the pinnacle of artistic achievement had passed, leaving posterity with a daunting inheritance, best symbolised by Beethoven. Awe and admiration of the past, once considered essential qualities in artistic production, were now perceived as paralysing obstacles. How could one measure up, without resorting to outmoded notions of imitation and derivation?

Johannes Brahms chose explicitly to face the challenge of history. He was fascinated by the past and not afraid to seek his own originality within an historical framework – both that of art music and folk music. He became profoundly interested in studying history – particularly the history of music – in part because he was an autodidact who felt his lack of a formal education acutely.

In terms of education and material well-being, the contrast between Brahms's background and

those of, for example, Mendelssohn and Schumann, both of whom Brahms greatly admired, is striking. Brahms overcompensated by becoming a more disciplined reader and systematic researcher than most, if not all, of his musical contemporaries. He cherished his friendship with members of the Viennese academic and intellectual élite.

As Brahms's own massive private library makes plain, his interests ranged widely, from philosophy to painting and art history – a field for which he reserved particular enthusiasm. Jacob Burckhardt's *Cicerone*, the famous guide to the art and architecture of Italy, was one of his favourite books. Late in life Brahms quarrelled with his dearest friend, Clara Schumann, over the work of Max Klinger, an artist whom Brahms admired. Klinger dedicated his cycle *Amor and Psyche* to the composer.

But Brahms's favourite enterprise after the mid-1870s, apart from composition, was his work in a systematic and scholarly fashion in reclaiming the past for his contemporaries and for posterity. He collected original manuscripts and first editions of Scarlatti, Haydn, Schubert and Wagner. He edited historically significant works, including the symphonies of Schubert for the first complete Schubert edition. He relished looking for and finding errors in printed editions of the Classical masters, and worked on new editions of Couperin, Handel and, above all, Schumann. He studied the history of music theory; Hugo Riemann, the eminent and prolific theorist, dedicated one of his books to Brahms.

He also became an expert in Renaissance and Baroque music. As the eminent musicologist Karl Geiringer observed, he correctly challenged the great scholar Spitta on the question of the authenticity of the *St Luke Passion*, then attributed to Bach. Brahms was severely critical of performances of Baroque music in his day – particularly those by Johann Herbeck, the handsome and charismatic Viennese choral conductor – for what Brahms regarded as a failure to take into account the history of performance practices. Most importantly, however, Brahms saw his own compositional work as part of a historical continuum which demanded both recognition of and respect for past models.

Brahms began his musical career

as a performer. Though the bulk of his public performances as a solo pianist was concentrated in his early years before his move to Vienna in the early 1860s, he continued to play the piano in public throughout his life. A lesser-known dimension of his performance career is his activity as a conductor. A cursory glance at the catalogue of his compositions indicates the legacy of many years spent conducting choirs. There is a wealth of stunning music for chorus,

which reflects the significant place of the amateur choral tradition in the musical life of the mid-nineteenth century. Brahms conducted both the Singakademie and the Singverein in Vienna, and in those roles he performed a great deal of Renaissance and Baroque music.

The apex of Brahms's career as a performer was his tenure as concert director of the Society of the Friends of Music, Vienna's leading musical institution, between the years 1872 and 1875. The Society maintained the Singverein and held a series of choral and instrumental concerts each season. Brahms succeeded Anton Rubinstein (for whom he had limited respect), then retired from his position after three years in order to devote himself exclusively to composition. Yet he continued to be active in the life of the Society, encouraging the growth of its archive and conservatory and working closely with its resident archivists and historians. He sat on the Society's board of directors for decades (a role that in some sense made him Bruckner's employer, since Bruckner was a member of the conservatory's faculty). Brahms bequeathed his not inconsiderable treasure of original manuscripts and books to the Society – a gift which still constitutes a crucial part of its legendary collection.

In his programmes with the Society, Brahms focused much of his attention on Baroque music,

particularly that of Bach and Handel, including Bach's Cantata No. 21, but also earlier music from Isaac to Schütz.

Brahms gave the first performance in Vienna of fragments from Schubert's A flat major Mass. Schubert occupied a particularly important place in Brahms's programmes. He orchestrated several Schubert songs, one of which he premiered in 1873. He also conducted Berlioz's *Harold in Italy* and Mendelssohn's secular cantata, *Die erste Walpurgisnacht*. Given the intensity with which Brahms struggled with the legacy of Beethoven, one might expect that he would have performed more of Beethoven's music. In fact, he

Left

Said to be Brahms singing his *Four Serious Songs*, in Frankfurt, where he attended Clara Schumann's funeral

Below left

Painting by Josef Novak

Royal College of Music. Historisches Museum der Stadt Wien/AKG Photo London conducted the *Missa Solemnis* and the Choral Fantasy, but no other works. He also did not shy away from presenting his own music, particularly the *Triumphlied*, the *Song of Destiny*, the Alto Rhapsody and the *German Requiem*. In the mid-1880s he toured with Hans von Bülow's famed Meiningen Orchestra, conducting his E minor Symphony, the Fourth.

Brahms was notorious for his acerbic wit, gruff exterior and exacting succinctness of expression. He was deeply self-critical and destroyed music of his own that he believed to be inadequate. He was equally quick to focus his acute powers of discrimination on others. This characteristic did not make him particularly popular among younger, aspiring composers, and led to the wildly negative fixations that two highly talented students at the conservatory – Hugo Wolf and Mahler's close friend Hans Rott – developed about him.

His critical view of contemporary composers was the result of his own deep-seated interior cultural pessimism. He believed that the vocation of a composer in the late nineteenth century was largely thankless. Indeed, it seemed increasingly difficult to write good music that was at once original and yet of a standard that could measure up to the achievements of the great masters of the Renaissance and the Baroque, or the work of the Viennese Classical composers and the generation of Chopin, Schumann

and Mendelssohn. Brahms deeply respected the gifts and accomplishments of his most successful contemporary, Richard Wagner; but he did not share Wagner's aesthetic strategy, which appeared to rob music of its autonomous logic and to pander to a less than discerning public by seducing them with a fantastic and excessive theatricality.

Brahms was profoundly a man of learning, yet free from the pretensions and mannerisms that are too often the result of university education. No composer of comparable stature in the traditional canon of European concert music can compare with him in the arena of musical historical scholarship. Few composers spent as much time poring over the music of past masters with as much care and devotion. In this centennial year of Brahms's death, the compositional achievement properly occupies centre stage, but it is well to remember that his development as a composer was profoundly influenced by his sustained and critical engagement with the history of music.

In turn, his constant references to history in his music, as well as his public advocacy of the music of the past as an indispensable source of taste and judgment, which informed his activities as conductor, collector and editor, all help us to mark the beginning of our own century's attitude towards the past. Our

ongoing obsession with a standard inherited repertory, the role that neo-Classicism has played in twentieth-century composition, and the growth of musicology, can all be traced back to Brahms. So, too, can this century's revival of so-called Early Music and its engagement with the history of past performance practices. It is, as Arnold Schoenberg wrote in the 1930s, surely therefore not only within the realm of musical composition that one must regard Brahms as a 'progressive'.

Relax

Meridian Audio is one of the world's leading companies in audio and video systems – everything from exceptional CD players to the most advanced digital surround sound systems.

We not only design and make our own products but write the software which controls them. So you can relax, all our products are designed as part of a matching system which is easy to use and can always be up to date.

Call or fax us for a brochure or visit our web page for the whole picture.

BOOTHROYD STUART
MERIDIAN©

Meridian Audio Limited Stonehill, Stukeley Meadows, Huntingdon, Cambridgeshire PE18 6ED
Tel **44** (0)1480 52144 Fax **44** (0)1480 459934

Meridian America Inc 3800 Camp Creek Parkway, Building 2400, Suite 112, Atlanta, GA 30331
Tel (404) 344 7111 Fax (404) 346 7111

http://www.meridian.co.uk

MOST UNUSUALLY in this century, when artists of all kinds have felt the need to justify their actions, Bartók said very little about why and how he did what he did. He was, in all things, reticent: almost everyone who knew him seems to have felt this to be a principal aspect of his personality, and the point is reinforced by his letters, which very rarely disclose personal matters, as well as by the many photographs in which he shows the same slightly

Bartók:
A new musical
language

Interpreted by
Paul Griffiths

anxious or severe but always unyielding front. He gives nothing away, except that perhaps through all these silences he says just one word. Listen.

That confidence – the confidence that his music could and would tell its own stories – presumes certain beliefs, which, after listening, we can begin to understand. One of those beliefs was certainly in the power of music to speak, and speak to all: this was by no means the only sense in which Bartók was Beethoven's heir. But any Romantic has to be also a Classicist, and just as impressive as

Bartók's rhetorical force is his delight in pattern and movement: the play of themes and figures, the swell and decline of harmonic tension, the different impulses of rhythm, all suggesting another belief, that the ear would be led – or more often driven or danced – through the music as it happened, as if the music contained all the rules necessary to its understanding.

Again, though, the opposite is also true. The music appeals as well to ancient rules, for it is the music of someone thoroughly versed in tradition – the tradition not only of the great Western masters (especially Bach and Beethoven) but also of the villages of central Europe and further afield, and it gains some of its power from its habit of telling us, in different ways, what we already know. So we come round to a new understanding of the lone Beethovenian genius. The ability to speak, on the most universal level, is not just a matter of having something to say, but of having a language in which to say it. Bartók shows us both these things, so that we might feel we are being addressed not so much by a man as by a dialect – a dialect that is new, strong and utterly distinctive.

The creation of such a dialect could not happen all at once. Bartók began as a child of the Austro-Hungarian Empire and of its essentially Germanic musical culture, which provided him with a certain measure he was to maintain

Right
Béla Bartók, 1938

Left Bartók plays Bartók: caricature by Aline Fruhaup, 1927

Below Béla Bartók and Zoltán Kodály in Kodály's home in Budapest

century, absorbing Richard Strauss and Max Reger. These imperatives and ambitions are loudly voiced in the big work he wrote at the end of his time as a student, the symphonic poem *Kossuth* (1903).

To move from hope to achievement, though, Bartók needed to go further, and around 1905 he made two discoveries that helped him on his way. One was the music of Debussy, which his friend Zoltán Kodály had brought back from Paris. The other was Hungarian folk music. From both he took the same messages: that there are numerous scales besides the major, minor and chromatic of the central Western tradition, and that there are numerous ways of counting rhythm other than as two, three or four beats in even bars and regular phrases. To explore these discoveries, he set himself to study all over again. He began collecting, transcribing and analysing folk music – work he was to pursue for the rest of his life. And he began creating his new dialect, at first largely in short piano pieces. Sometimes these would be simple arrangements of folk tunes, suitable for children (for Bartók saw that the development of a Hungarian music required the development of a

throughout his life. For him, as for Beethoven and Brahms, big instrumental forms were paramount (though he might have had other reasons, too, for his reluctance to write vocal music: a distrust of words, and perhaps a worry that settings of Hungarian would not gain wide dissemination). However, he also knew from an early age that he had to be a specifically Hungarian composer: hence his decision to study not in Vienna but in Budapest, and hence the importance to him of Liszt. Not only that, he knew too that he had to be a specifically modern composer, which meant, around the turn of the

Hungarian musical culture, lived and breathed from an early age) – though even the simplest arrangement might offer, for him and for us, lessons in how to harmonise and counterpoint a melody. Sometimes the connection with folk music would be more indirect, stimulated by the experience of analysing tonalities, melodic shapes, ornamentations and rhythms.

The First World War disrupted Bartók's collecting expeditions, and his few trips thereafter were to more exotic locations: Turkey and North Africa. There were several reasons for the change. One was that the old peasant music, captured in Bartók's notebooks and on his phonograph recordings, was fast dying in the postwar Europe of increased travel and communication. Another was that the pressing need now was to sort and publish what had been collected; and yet another may have been that Bartók preferred these scholarly tasks, which were satisfying in themselves, and from which he could learn a lot about how to form and vary musical motifs.

But also there was his sense that patriotism was not enough. The

Left Bartók and his second wife, pianist Ditta Pásztory

Below The Hungarian hero Kossuth, subject of Bartók's 1903 symphonic poem (Prom 25)

AKG Photo London

Right
Bartók on the cover of
a Hungarian magazine,
1935

Bottom right
Caricature of Bartók
from the *Radio Times*
18 May 1934

war could have taught him that truth; so could the disappointments he and Kodály suffered when their new Hungarian music failed to gain more than a marginal place in Hungarian musical life: for several years he abjured Budapest's concert halls in despair. Yet perhaps even more important was what his cherished folk music itself was

diatonic melody of the Second Violin Concerto (1937–8) – and Stravinsky, to whom Bartók could relate much more directly. Following Stravinsky he began writing ballets: *The Wooden Prince* (1914–17) and *The Miraculous Mandarin* (1918–19). On Stravinsky's example, too, he honed his feeling for the piano as a percussion instrument – a feeling important to his First Piano

in our lives – Bartók's dialect speaks with a particular relevance. It speaks of retaining old truths, but only after their contents and implications have been explored in a contemporary context. It speaks of accepting new ideas, but only where they can measure up to what we already know. It speaks of valuing the local as part of the universal, and the universal as part of the local. It speaks of these possibilities. It does not say they will be easy.

Above, from left
András Schiff plays the
First Piano Concerto
and other works in
Prom 35
Pierre Boulez conducts
the Four Pieces for
Orchestra in Prom 31
Viktoria Mullova plays
the Second Violin
Concerto in Prom 33
Neeme Järvi conducts
the Concerto for
Orchestra in Prom 67

telling him: that musical ideas are ignorant of national boundaries, and that any nation's folk music is not its own permanent possession but a repertory that has evolved through contacts with neighbours. The richness he prized in Hungarian folk music was the triumph not just of Magyars but of Romanians, Slovaks, Bulgarians, Ruthenians, Croats and Slovenes. His own music, too, would be a unique synthesis.

More now went into the melting-pot, including Schoenberg – whose music, fascinatingly alien to Bartók, prompted responses from the near atonality of the Four Orchestral Pieces (1912) to the twelve-note

Concerto (1926). However, the title of that work gives the game away. Unlike Stravinsky, Bartók was linked to the Austro-German tradition and to its favoured genres, including the solo concerto and the string quartet, and nearly all his major works after *The Miraculous Mandarin* are in standard formats, if not exactly standard forms. His dialect retained accents from Vienna alongside others that had come from Hungarian folk music, and through that from an immemorial human past.

Now – more than fifty years after his death, and at a time of confusion about the place tradition must have

Barbican
Great Performers
Great Orchestras and Celebrity Recitals

Les Arts Florissants with William Christie
perform theatre music by Charpentier, Monteverdi and Purcell.
18 - 21 September

Schumann Revealed - Part 2
John Eliot Gardiner conducts the **Orchestre Révolutionnaire et Romantique** in a weekend of concerts exploring the music of Robert Schumann.
3 - 5 October

Schubert - A Contemporary Celebration
Gidon Kremer combines Schubert's chamber music with contemporary works inspired by Schubert.
22 October, 12 November, 12 December

Great Orchestras of the World
St Petersburg Philharmonic Orchestra
Yuri Temirkanov conductor
Programme to be confirmed
21 October

Royal Concertgebouw Orchestra
Nikolaus Harnoncourt conductor
Works by Schubert
9 November

Group Dynamics - International Chamber Orchestras
Amsterdam Baroque Orchestra
Ton Koopman conductor
Cantatas by J.S. Bach
1 October

St Paul Chamber Orchestra
Hugh Wolff conductor
Richard Goode piano
Works by Wagner, Mozart, Bolcom and Copland
10 October

Barbican Celebrity Recitals
Kyung-Wha Chung violin
15 October

Gidon Kremer violin
22 October

Chilingirian Quartet
5 November

Mikhail Pletnev piano
16 November

Evelyn Glennie percussion
9 December

For a free colour brochure giving full details, including discounts of up to 35%, telephone the Box Office now.

Barbican Centre
Box Office 0171 638 8891 (9am-8pm daily)

The Barbican Centre is owned, funded and managed by the Corporation of London.

CORPORATION OF LONDON

'To be played with love later on'

Philip Brett on Britten today

IN JULY 1941, the Canadian composer Colin McPhee wrote to Britten's American benefactress, Elizabeth Mayer, about their mutual friend: 'If he is only wanting a career (and I know that is not it), and a career that I know would be very short, then he need not change. But if he wants to survive, to be played with love later on, even during the later years of his life, he must search deeper for a more personal, more *interesting* idiom. Alas, this is so; in the order of today good craftsmanship is *not* enough'. McPhee also makes it clear that Aaron Copland joined him in wanting to make the young Britten see 'the futility of certain things'.

It has sometimes been assumed that the British critics' initial response to Britten – that his music was too clever by half and, by implication, heartless – was the result of insular and perhaps homophobic attitudes, stemming from the determined amateurism embedded in English composition, and the gruff masculinism of English ruralism and pastoralism. McPhee allows us to see that similar reservations were held by two intelligent transatlantic composers who also shared Britten's sexual orientation.

In recent years an almost opposite interpretation has arisen. The Britten of the 1930s is often celebrated now as an eclectic, open,

Right
Peter Pears in front
of Britten's portrait

Above
War Requiem rehearsal,
Coventry, 1962

Malcolm Crowthers Hulton Getty

outward-looking composer, redressing the insularity of the Pastoral School by boldly looking abroad for techniques, forms and idioms. Some influential critics bemoan his turning, after his return to England, into what they represent as an increasingly closed-minded provincial composer – his style thinning with age until it was completely desiccated and lacking in emotional conviction.

The works themselves, of course, each have individual inflections that contradict such broad generalisations, as Britten Weekend at the Proms will show. The British choral tradition obviously lies behind the early *A Boy was Born*, for example, though the resulting sound is often drier than Vaughan Williams, Ireland and others. Much of its technique reveals Britten's orientation as a largely orchestral and chamber-music composer in the 1930s, for it notably lacks the sense of vocal style which seems so natural by the time of *Rejoice in the Lamb* that we tend to think of it as innate.

The American visit of 1939–42 was clearly a major turning-point. Reading E. M. Forster's article on George Crabbe, the eighteenth-century Aldeburgh poet, Britten realised that he also was among those who needed to work with their roots, both national and personal. The rejection of *Paul Bunyan* by the New York critics, and the unsympathetic cultural surroundings in which he found himself, even the

friendly criticism of McPhee and Copland, must have triggered off in him a set of musical decisions linked to those of career.

Around this time Britten wrote for the American journal *Modern Music* a short article entitled 'England and the Folk-Art Problem'. In this he projects Parry and Elgar as the binary opposition haunting English composition, the one having 'stressed the amateur idea and ... encouraged folk-art', the other emphasising 'the importance of technical efficiency' and welcoming 'any foreign influences that can be profitably assimilated'. Studiously avoiding any mention of Holst and Vaughan Williams, Britten names Walton, Lambert, Maconchy, Berkeley, Christian Darnton, Lutyens, Rawsthorne and (with reservations) Howard Ferguson and Rubbra as indicating that 'since 1930 the influence of Parry has largely disappeared'. All this was presumably a direct contradiction of Vaughan Williams's famous statement about composers 'who thought that their own country was not good enough for them and went off in the early stages to become little Germans or little Frenchmen'.

If Vaughan Williams was seen as the enemy, he also had to be taken seriously as someone who had achieved the position of chief national composer. To reach similar status Britten would have to distinguish his work from that of his older compatriot but also, I think he

Top left
Britten and Pears, Canada, 1957

Bottom left
Britten, Aaron Copland and Peter Pears in upstate New York, 1939

Right from top
Martin Neary directing members of the Choir of Westminster Abbey (Prom 39)

War Requiem soloists (Prom 40):
Hans Peter Blochwitz
Eva Urbanová
Thomas Hampson

realised, imitate his methods. It is during the American period that Britten began to make folk-song arrangements for later publication.

Realisations of Purcell songs, which attached Britten to his seventeenth-century heritage in a manner similar to Vaughan Williams's identification with the Tudor school, came a little later. These pieces fulfilled more than the practical need of material for recitals with his partner, Peter Pears. One of Britten's most successful pieces written on his return to England was the Serenade for Tenor, Horn and Strings, in which a beatific vision of the past, and of the countryside, replaced the acerbic Auden-inspired critique of the earlier *Our Hunting Fathers*. Both *Peter Grimes* and *Billy Budd* gave a new face to the favourite pastoralist topic of the sea. And the substitution of Aldeburgh, Suffolk and East Anglia for Hereford, Gloucestershire and the West Country was further aided by the founding of the Aldeburgh Festival in 1948.

The composition of the *War Requiem* seems to summarise the strategy in a particularly eloquent way: as an English oratorio it fits right into the native tradition (Handel, Elgar, Vaughan Williams); as a pacifist statement it was marked with Britten's own social and personal concerns, placed above politics in a religious context.

Strategy alone would never have worked as a means of reaching the

lofty goal Britten set for himself. More important is the personal voice he found by connecting his life to his music in radical and interesting ways. The change can almost be pinpointed to the *Ceremony of Carols* and *Hymn to St Cecilia*, written on board ship during the return to England in 1942. These pieces strike a poised and classic (rather than neo-Classic) attitude – at its best simple (not simplistic) and restrained (not restricted). In *Rejoice in the Lamb*, written while the *Grimes* libretto was being sorted out, the anger of the oppressed, stemming ultimately from Britten's own alienated social experience as a homosexual, was framed in such a way as to universalise its meaning, a feat that *Peter Grimes* itself brought to perfection.

With the overwhelming success of the opera, Britten found his inimitable voice as a composer, for better or worse. But having reached such a state comparatively early, he was able to turn his back on eclecticism and to ignore a great deal of other music. In a manner found shocking at the time, but radical now, he took some ideas from serialism in a way that made nonsense of its central tenets; and then, in *Owen Wingrave*, used it as a means of representing militaristic evil, the music of old, contentious Europe. In the meantime he had rediscovered the music of Bali and the musical drama of Japan, elements of which he used to portray

the 'innocence' he always sought, particularly in the 'church parables', little operas of which *The Prodigal Son* is the least familiar, invoking the Western mystery play.

Something may have been lost in the process, of course, but more was gained. Twenty years ago few would have envisaged the downfall of the progressive ideals of musical Modernism that has taken place at an accelerating rate in the present decade. Today it is not composers of one party line or another who are celebrated, but those who, whatever their stylistic practices and national or institutional affiliations, remained in some sense true to themselves and to an effective vision of what music could achieve in the twentieth century. In searching within himself for issues with which to deal in his music, particularly his rather complicated set of homoerotic preoccupations and their wider social implications and connections, and in remaining identifiably English and sufficiently apart from contemporary developments, Britten managed to exceed expectations, even his own. In spite of biographical revelations of the sort that send conventional 'classical' musicians and music lovers into orbit, his music more than survives; indeed 'played with love later on', and listened to with love by people all over the world.

The Proms celebrate Britten with a weekend of concerts in Proms 37 to 40

THE
LAST NIGHT
OF THE
PROMS

15656 91912

ORIGINAL LIVE
RECORDINGS FROM
THE BBC

Tune in to some of the world's best known brands

GRAND METROPOLITAN

....adding value

An American
vernacular

Wilfrid Mellers considers some of the varied influences that make up America's plural musical language

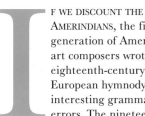

IF WE DISCOUNT THE AMERINDIANS, the first generation of American art composers wrote eighteenth-century European hymnody with interesting grammatical errors. The nineteenth-century generations made more 'correct' church music and streamlined instrumental music according to Teutonic recipes – flourishing or floundering in polite parlours, genteel universities, and on the public concert circuits. Yet as soon as 'America' began to establish its polymorphous identities, it was hardly surprising that composers in a New World should have wanted to Make It New. The 'real' American composers now seem to be the grand old pioneers: of whom the most representative and most impressive

is Charles Ives, who was born in 1874, died in 1954, and wrote virtually no music after the early 1920s, mainly through ill-health, possibly of psychosomatic origins, since he was not only neglected but reviled.

Whatever his ultimate stature, one can legitimately claim that Ives was the first great composer of democratic principle, responsive alike to European artistic traditions and to the multifarious world around him: which in musical terms meant the hymns, marches, parlour ballads and shanty-town rags of Danbury, Connecticut.

When in a later generation an American composer appeared who sought, and achieved, complete artistic realisation, he could do so only by a severe limitation of range. That composer was Aaron Copland;

and to refer to his limitation of range is not a pejorative remark. Both Copland's limitation and Ives's incompleteness were part of the integrity that makes them the two key figures in American music.

Ives was born in small-town America; Copland was born, in the year of the century, 1900, in a 'drab street' (his own expression) in Brooklyn. That Copland was a big city boy, whereas Ives was a small-town boy, has more than biographical interest. Copland grew up in the polyglot industrial society that was no more than latent in Ives's world. Unselfconsciously, Ives accepted the materials his world offered him, stayed at home, and expressed his rebellion by making anew the world he loved. Copland absorbed the temper of big city life at a level below consciousness; being

aware that he was alone (and 'original') he needed a technique to establish identity; so, as a self-reliant Jewish Brooklyn youth, he saved enough money to study 'abroad' – but not in Germany, wherein the American nineteenth-century musical tradition had been nurtured, but in Paris where, under the guidance of Nadia Boulanger, he could purge his music of 'old' European dross and discover a tough, bare idiom adaptable to the lonesomeness of big cities. Significantly, the major European composer who offered most to this purgative process was the cosmopolitan, deracinated, Russian Outsider, Stravinsky.

The key work in this process is the Piano Variations of 1930. Copland produced, in the early 1930s, a few other works comparable with the Variations, but he understandably came to feel a need for wider communication than was possible through his boldly lonely music. In the mid-1930s he therefore deliberately turned to the creation of music for radio, cinema and the ballet.

We are to hear the first of Copland's ballets this season. Written in 1938 – just before the outbreak of the Second World War – *Billy the Kid* is directly about the conflict between Society and the Outlaw. Billy was a historical figure who became mythical. At the age of eleven he stabbed a man who had shot his mother in a brawl, later capping this by shooting a man who, in a Wild West tavern, accused him of dishonesty at cards. After a gun-battle between Billy's gang and the Sheriff's posse, Billy is captured and gaoled, but escapes from prison, to join his Mexican girlfriend in the solitudinous desert. He is betrayed to the Sheriff by an Indian guide – racial otherness seems to be both good (the lover) and bad (the guide). Lighting a cigarette, Billy is shot by the Sheriff; and the ballet ends as it began with a march of pioneers, striding westwards with the Sheriff at their head.

Copland's music came to full maturity in a fusion of the uncompromising honesty of the Piano Variations with the more relaxed manner of the ballets and film music: here the key work is the Piano Sonata of 1939–41, in which

his urban and rural manners coalesce. During these years he evolved a plain American vernacular on which innumerable lesser composers, and some non-composers, gratefully drew. One of Copland's immediate contemporaries, however, seemed initially to rival him in potency, if not ultimately in staying power. He was Roy Harris, born in 1898, not in New York City, but in the Oklahoma Panhandle, and of Scotch-Irish parents who had built their own log-cabin in the Cimarron frontier rush; one of his grandfathers had been a Kansas circuit rider, the other a rider in the Pony Express from Chicago to the Western ports. Despite this pioneering background, and a career that started in farming, Roy had intellectual abilities that took him to study, along with Copland, under Nadia Boulanger in Paris. Yet from the start his music explored, with hard economy, a rural-pioneering vein which culminated, in 1933, in the making of one of the central American masterpieces, his one-movement Third Symphony.

The vision of empty distances the music evokes, the sense of growth and endeavour in the mere length of the line, suggest man alone in the wilderness; the music is 'religious' in that the spontaneously evolving monody sounds like a rudimentary, open-air plainchant, God-given in creativity; while it is modern, and specifically American, in the speech-inflected plasticity of its phrasing,

and in its harmonic fluidity. As the unbroken textures flow on, the music enacts the evolution of a civilisation.

Although Harris never composed another work with such punch and pertinence, this Third Symphony is still a masterpiece, telling us that, though we have lost our religious innocence, we know what is at stake.

Roy Harris died in 1979, in his early eighties. Another pioneering composer – now in his eighties – is Elliott Carter who, in an early piece like *Holiday Overture*, seemed a shade *too* indebted to Copland. Around the age of forty, however, he began to make a 'morphologically' exploratory music that relates him to Ives, the Cello Sonata of 1948 forming a bridge to his first fully realised masterpiece, the First String Quartet of 1951. Since then, he has been in the vanguard of American music, creating strenuously 'difficult' works concerned with the wellsprings of life, even in a world as tortuously tangled as ours. The new *Allegro scorrevole* for orchestra is likely to challenge and excite.

Carter, like Ives, is a New Englander; another octogenarian, Lou Harrison is, as a Californian looking West towards Asia, Carter's opposite but complementary pole. He studied briefly with Schoenberg when the Austrian was exiled in Los Angeles, but his interest in him must have been for his linear independence rather than for his Expressionist harmonic fervour, for

Above Elliott Carter

Right, from top
Michael Gordon
Philip Glass
Steve Reich

Below
Lou Harrison

Harrison is much closer to his first mentor the wild-boy Henry Cowell, who experimented with sounds coaxed from a battered upright piano stored in a shed in the woods, and to his friend and colleague John Cage, arch-apostle of sounds 'in themselves' and of silence. Harrison's aesthetic, too, tends to be more oriental than occidental; he has movingly said that the function of music – his own, as well as that of Java and Bali – is to 'consider, conserve, cherish, create'.

In Prom 32 we'll hear one of his large-scale works, the Suite for Symphonic Strings, first performed in 1960, but containing material harking back to 1936, when Harrison was nineteen. The piece is now titled 'New First Suite for Strings': a nomenclature that apparently means that the work has been substantially recast. His festive Concerto for Organ and Percussion, meanwhile, is scheduled for Prom 3.

Ives, an Old Pioneer, looked forward to an unknown but not unknowable future; Lou Harrison, a New Pioneer, looked back in order to 'mieux sauter'. There's a similar process in so-called Process, or Minimal, music, initially explored by Steve Reich who, rather than wilfully asserting identity, sought identification with the tribe by adapting to urban industrial technology procedures picked up 'in the field' from African, Moroccan, Balinese and Jewish 'musics of necessity' – as in *Music for Mallet*

Instruments, Voices and Organ. An alienated Jew and urban New Yorker, Reich has helped us to survive in our asphalt jungle, much as indigenous ethnic peoples use music to counter the threat of the real forest. Gradually, Reich earned international celebrity because he offered a potential 'new start'. When he admitted words and dance into his musically corporeal techniques, he equated ritual with theatrical illusion, creating, in *Tehillim,* an Eastern Hebraic fiesta, apposite to a non-practising New York Jew, in which we may participate vicariously.

With Reich's disciple and colleague Philip Glass, the transition from electro-percussive ritual to the quasi-operatic 'show' is complete, as he becomes not so much a composer as a maker of pseudo-rituals working in co-operation with singing and dancing priests and priestesses, and with magician-scientists in the control room. He has become even more 'fabulously' successful, with a fairly young public, than Reich; and it's understandable that such new primitivism should rival rock-pop in appeal and should also – to use Conrad's memorable phrase – 'in the destructive element immerse'. Much Heavy Metal music comes into this category: as does some of the work of Frank Zappa who, for his uncompromising intelligence and honest desperation, deserves inclusion in these concerts. Zappa's ritual music-theatre is at once anciently satyric and modernly satirical.

One might say the same of a new work, also to be performed in Prom 3, by the youngest composer represented. Michael Gordon is a 'crossover' composer in a sense even more radical than that of Reich, Glass or Zappa: for Gordon was born way down in Florida, out on a limb from the 'United' States, and grew up in a Nicaraguan jungle on the outskirts of Managua. In further paradox he also received formal musical training at Yale, under Martin Bresnick, while entering active music-making through underground rock groups in New York City. Like Glass, he has founded his own ensemble, with the crossover title of the Michael Gordon Philharmonic, touring with it throughout America and Europe. His activities have become, strictly speaking, global, for he has also worked with the London group Icebreaker, and since 1991 has collaborated with the video artist Eliot Camian, producing video 'operas' in Vienna and Frankfurt as well as New York City. Currently, Gordon is director of New York's 'Bang on a Can' Festival.

The works by Zappa and Michael Gordon are being conducted by John Adams, who will present in the same concert the UK premiere of his own recent piece, *Scratchband.* Perhaps because he's a decade younger than Reich and Glass (but quite a bit older than Gordon), Adams gets the balance between ritual and theatre about right. Far from totally

rejecting 'Western' traditions, he welcomes our multifarious pluralism, 'feeding not just on minimalism but Berg, Stravinsky, rock 'n' roll, doo-wap music, Arabian music, Jewish music ... It makes it really fun to compose now, so long as you don't let those theoreticians get you down'.

Reich and Glass are now astonishingly sexagenarians, while even the beneficent, often joyful Adams has attained the half century. Another BBC commission goes to another sexagenarian, Roger Reynolds who, like Varèse, was initially trained in mathematical engineering, but in 1960 founded the ONCE group of avant-garde musicians at Ann Arbor. Studying with Ross Lee Finney, a post-Schoenbergian serialist, and with the Spanish-British part-time serialist Roberto Gerhard, Reynolds was for a time a global wanderer. When he returned to the US in 1969 he became a West Coast composer, teaching at San Diego University, where he fashioned a personal idiom stemming from serialism, but subordinating its rigour to 'the

rewards of flow and process'. Mathematically determined pitch-sets are combined with 'accelerating and retarding temporal proportions logarithmically derived', and with computer-manipulated sounds. But if a verbal account of Reynolds's music makes him sound like a musician-scientist-priest of the Global Village, the effect of his sounds is still youthfully magical: not as spiritually elevating as Harrison's music nor as much 'fun' as Adams's, but undeniably a renewal of the spirit.

Comparably a 'between worlds' man, Stephen Montague was born in Syracuse, NY, in 1943, and initially studied with a very 'straight' opera composer, Carlisle Floyd. At Ohio State University, however, he graduated into electrophonics, which he further explored on a Fulbright scholarship that took him to Warsaw. Yet if this bolstered his avant-garde credentials, it didn't prevent his settling down in 'old' England where, beginning in 1974, he worked with the Strider Dance Company, evolving his own brand of Reichian minimalism. His influence on British avant-garde music has been generously benign, and it may be pertinent that one of his most successful works should be a ballet for the (usually orthodox) Sadler's Wells Company.

One other composer, Colin McPhee, just about qualifies for inclusion because, although born in Canada as long ago as 1900, he went to Bali in the 1930s, fired by

recordings of its music, and then returned to the New World to live, as an American citizen, in New York. While in Bali he wrote a big book about its music that has become a classic, and a small book about the Good Life that Bali might offer to alcoholic city-worn Americans like himself. Though the Edenic panacea didn't work out, the transcriptions McPhee made of Balinese gamelan music for two (equal tempered) pianos had some influence on a composer of genius, Benjamin Britten, in his *The Prince of the Pagodas* and church parables; while McPhee himself managed to produce, in 1936, one work that effectively adapted the technique of Balinese gamelan to modern European instruments. *Tabuh-tabuhan* has modestly maintained a place in the repertory, as a vivacious hybrid between gamelan music and something rather like Latin-American jazz, offering a foretaste of Glass-y minimalism.

American music features prominently in Proms 3, 21, 32, 49 and 51

The Lexus LS400. (Not to be confused with John Cage's 4´ 33.˝)

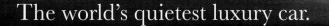

The world's quietest luxury car.

LEXUS

Call 0800 34 34 34.

Principal: Curtis Price

Royal Academy of Music
celebrates its
175th Anniversary in 1997

Many famous musicians - singers, players, conductors, composers, teachers - have studied at the Academy during its 175 years, not the least of them being Sir Henry Wood himself, who also taught at the Academy. Today, Academy alumni can be found throughout the world as leaders in their chosen branches of the music profession.

For a Diary of Events at the Academy, or for a Prospectus and details of admission to the Academy, please write to the Development Office, Royal Academy of Music (P), Marylebone Road, London NW1 5HT
Tel: 0171 873 7333
Fax: 0171 873 7334

dartington
college
of
arts

BA *honours*

music

**performance
writing**

theatre

**visual
performance**

**arts
management**

MPhil and **PhD**

Dartington College of Arts
Totnes, Devon TQ9 6EJ England
Tel +44 (0)1803 862224
Fax +44 (0)1803 863569

Registered as a Charity No. 900054

APPLAUSE?

THE MUSICIANS BENEVOLENT FUND CAN DO SO MUCH TO HELP NEEDY MUSICIANS AND THEIR DEPENDANTS – FOR WHOM APPLAUSE IS A DISTANT MEMORY. SO REMEMBER THE JOY THAT MUSIC HAS BROUGHT YOU. PLEASE SEND US A DONATION AND CONSIDER REMEMBERING US IN YOUR WILL.

MUSICIANS
BENEVOLENT FUND

MUSICIANS BENEVOLENT FUND, ROOM PG1, 16 OGLE STREET, LONDON W1P 8JB. REGISTERED CHARITY No. 228089

THERE IS A certain fascination about the last major works written by composers still at the height of their powers, but nevertheless aware that their last masterpiece is at hand.

Unlike Mozart, who did not live to complete his *Requiem*, Handel managed to finish *Jephtha* in 1751, but it was a struggle. He began the score with his usual fluency but, having reached the last chorus of Part Two on 13 February, he had to lay it aside because of his deteriorating eyesight. The completion of the remainder stretched over several months, and Handel added the final touches on the last day of August. The appearance of his autograph bears eloquent testimony to the physical effort which the work entailed.

The story of the oratorio, taken from the Book of Judges, revolves around Jephtha's vow that, if he defeated the Ammonites in battle, he would make an immediate sacrifice to Jehovah of the first animal or person that he saw: on his victorious return, the designated victim was his own daughter.

Handel's progress on the score had been dramatically halted in the midst of the powerful chorus 'How dark, O Lord, are thy decrees', and it is not too fanciful to imagine that the composer found some identification with Jephtha, at that moment distraught and bewildered by the apparent workings of God's providence.

The subject-matter of *Jephtha* (like that of its immediate predecessor *Theodora*) is concerned with the extent to which individuals are in control of their own destinies, and is played out in a drama involving well-developed characters. Thomas Morell, Handel's librettist, created a (moderately) happy ending to provide a suitably positive

Dark decrees

sentimental conclusion to the drama, but possibly also with a view to interpreting the Jephtha story as one example from a broad sweep of 'salvation' stories in Judaeo-Christian scriptures.

Morell's *Jephtha* libretto is to that extent controversial, but there is no question that it provided Handel with excellent material for musical setting, and that the composer responded with unusual warmth in his score. We do not go to Handel's *Jephtha* (or Mozart's *Requiem*) simply because it was the last major work of a great composer, but for the glorious musical experience that the work provides, and its sensitive treatment of a powerful human drama.

Sir Charles Mackerras conducts Handel's Jephtha *in Prom 58*

Donald Burrows introduces the last of Handel's great dramatic oratorios

Left 'Jephtha sees his daughter' by Giovanni Francesco Romanelli

Below
Joan Rodgers (Iphis)
Sir Charles Mackerras
Anthony Rolfe Johnson
(Jephtha)

THERE ARE FEW wittier, more stylish, or more finely-honed comic operas than Rossini's *Count Ory*. Rossini wrote the work for the Paris Opéra in 1828, his fancy having been hugely tickled by a saucy one-act vaudeville about the amorous voyagings of Count Ory, a real-life Medieval philanderer.

Champagne from Glyndebourne

Richard Osborne previews a welcome revival of a sparkling comedy

The authors of the show, Scribe and Delestre-Poirson, the kind of people who nowadays would be writing scripts for things like *Four Weddings and a Funeral*, were only too happy to turn their one-act vaudeville into a two-act opera. Like all good writers of sitcom, they knew they did not need to invent a new scenario, merely embellish the old one. Thus in the opera, the libidinous Count twice attempts to gain entry to the Castle of Formoutiers in order to win and woo the lovely young Countess Adèle, whose brother is away on a Crusade.

On the first occasion, Ory and his crew appear in the guise of a hermit and his disciples. That having failed, they return disguised as nuns – roistering nuns when they discover the castle's well-stocked wine cellars.

But it was not only Scribe and Delestre-Poirson who were giving a favourite show a new lease of life. Rossini, too, had pages of prime material sitting on his desk awaiting a more permanent home than the lavish and sophisticated entertainment he had concocted in the summer of 1825 for the celebrations surrounding the coronation in Rheims of King Charles X. Coronations don't happen every year (least of all in France) and Rossini was not a man to see fine ingredients go to waste.

The adaptation of material from *The Journey to Rheims* is masterly. And there is new music, too; music whose

Left
Portrait of Rossini in 1820 by Constance Mayer La Martinière

Below, from top
Andrew Davis conducts *Count Ory*
Annick Massis sings Countess Adèle
Tracey Welborn sings the Count

sensuous allure left contemporary composers open-mouthed with wonderment, not least Berlioz, whose own highly individual sound-world is openly anticipated by Rossini in the opera's exquisite Act 2 Trio. Happily, Berlioz was sport enough to admit it. 'There are', he said, 'diverse beauties here, that ingeniously parcelled out would suffice to make the fortune not of one but of two or three operas!'

Count Ory ushered in the great age of irreverent French musical comedy, sharpening a tradition begun by Auber and pointing the way to the sophisticated comic masterpieces of Offenbach, Chabrier, and Reynaldo Hahn. Later, when Rossini's reputation was in the doldrums, Liszt sprang to the opera's rescue by arranging a staging in Weimar. 'Its melodies', he said, 'flow like champagne.'

In 1954, prompted by the conductor Vittorio Gui, Glyndebourne famously revived the opera: a legendary production that set the champagne, musical and actual, flowing in copious quantities. Forty years on, all we can reasonably do is reach for the ice-bucket and say 'welcome back'.

Andrew Davis conducts Glyndebourne Festival Opera in Count Ory *in Prom 50*

Venetian sunshine

Andrew Lamb previews Gilbert and Sullivan's *The Gondoliers*

A S BEFITS ITS Venetian setting, *The Gondoliers* is Sullivan's sunniest score. Produced at the Savoy Theatre on 7 December 1889, it was the twelfth of the fourteen Gilbert and Sullivan comic operas and their last big success. Sullivan had long agitated to be free from what he saw as the strait-jacket of comic opera in order to satisfy his more serious ambitions. Finally liberated by a commission to write the grand opera *Ivanhoe*, he poured his melodic resource into *The Gondoliers* with a fluency that even he had rarely matched.

The score opens with a joyous outpouring of almost twenty minutes of continuous music in which the young gondoliers Marco and Giuseppe Palmieri demonstrate their democratic beliefs by choosing their brides Tessa and Gianetta blindfolded from amongst their pretty female companions. Then we meet the typically Gilbertian character of the henpecked Duke of Plaza-Toro, who 'led his regiment from behind, he found it less exciting'. From the formidable Grand Inquisitor, Don Alhambra, we learn that one of the newly married gondoliers is actually the King of Barataria. The future King was farmed out at birth and brought up with a gondolier's son, and only their former nursemaid can identify which is which. Until she is found, the two gondoliers must leave their wives and rule Barataria jointly. This they duly do, in a manner true to their republican principles. Finally, in true Gilbertian style, it transpires that the true King is neither of them, but rather the Duke of Plaza-Toro's servant, Luiz.

By then Sullivan has enchanted us with further joyous numbers – the idyllic Act 1 finale beginning with Tessa's plaintive 'Kind sir, you cannot have the heart' as the two wives bid farewell to their new husbands; Giuseppe's account of his royal duties, 'Rising early in the morning'; Marco's liltingly beautiful 'Take a pair of sparkling eyes'; the lively cachucha; the marvellous quartet 'In a contemplative fashion', in which lyricist and composer brilliantly portray the conflicting emotions of the four newly-weds; and the Duke's lesson in court etiquette 'I am a courtier grave and serious'. This is truly Gilbert and Sullivan at their very happiest.

Barry Wordsworth conducts a distinguished cast in The Gondoliers *in Prom 18*

Left
Kullervo's Curse (1899),
oil on canvas, painted in
the Wilderness Studio
Kallela by the Finnish
artist Akseli Gallen-Kallela
Top right Portrait
of Sibelius by
Akseli Gallen-Kallela
Below right
A Wood Nymph (1886),
by Robert Poetzelberger
Bottom left
Osmo Vänskä

David Nice introduces Sibelius's early choral symphony, and the London premiere of a rediscovered not neglected tone-poem

W E HAVE A potent national mythology to thank for the early flowering of Sibelius's essentially rugged style. It was only after several years of composing nothing but chamber works that the twenty-five-year-old composer turned to the medium of the symphony orchestra; but the *Kullervo* Symphony of 1892 already shows a vivid imagination fully fledged, obeying not strict musical laws but poetic ones.

Kullervo, one of several heroes in Finland's national epic the *Kalevala*, is born under a malign star. Like Wagner's Siegmund, he makes love to his sister; but unlike Siegmund, he does so inadvertently, and knowledge of the deed brings disaster to both of them. Sibelius depicts Kullervo's miserable youth with dark scoring for strings and winds of startling originality, while the sister-seduction is the dramatic high-point of the score. It features a

bracing sleigh-ride, a graphic if baleful orchestral sex-scene which anticipates the raw power of Janáček's operas, and two powerfully operatic laments from sister and brother when they learn the truth.

That striking movement was the only one to be played during Sibelius's lifetime once he had banned all performances after 1893, turning his back on the strict programmatic basis he had only recently pronounced as the true spur to creativity. *Kullervo and his Sister* resurfaced in the 1935 celebrations marking the 100th anniversary of the *Kalevala*'s first printed edition; but the symphony as a whole had to wait another twenty-three years for a complete performance.

Another symphonic narrative, *The Wood Nymph* – composed two years after *Kullervo*, with its roots in an even stranger Nordic tale told

by the Swedish poet Viktor Rydberg – fared better while Sibelius was alive, before disappearing from sight until recently. Only the chance mishap that it was never published can explain *The Wood Nymph*'s neglect; for it starts with a Sibelian epic adventure every inch as dynamic as the changing landscapes of *Lemminkäinen's Journey* and the wonderful *En Saga*, continues with a forest mystery as haunting as that of the late, great *Tapiola* and ends in disconsolate tragedy. 'The heart that is stolen by a wood nymph is never returned', writes the poet; and Sibelius realises Rydberg's haunting incantation with precocious orchestral mastery.

Osmo Vänskä conducts The Wood Nymph, Kullervo *and* Luonnotar *in an all-Sibelius programme in Prom 44*

Myths from the North

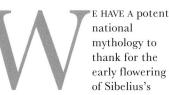

Left, main picture
Erich Wolfgang
Korngold in 1916
Left inset
Paul Daniel, who
conducts 'Violanta'
Above
Maria Jeritza, the first
Violanta
Janice Cairns sings the
title-role

Voluptuous Violanta

Brendan Carroll introduces a rare revival of a sumptuous late-Romantic opera

KORNGOLD WAS just seventeen when he composed his second opera *Violanta* in 1914, and it remains one of the most remarkable examples of musical precocity in history. By then he was already a veteran, having begun to compose at the age of six. He was proclaimed a genius by Gustav Mahler – an opinion shared by many, including Richard Strauss and Puccini – and by the time he wrote this opera, the greatest artists and conductors of the time were clamouring to perform his works, including Henry Wood at the 1912 Proms.

Korngold was Jewish, and the rise of Nazism interrupted his career, but he found a new challenge in Hollywood in the 1930s and 1940s, where he pioneered symphonic film scores, winning two Oscars. After the war, an attempt to revive his career failed, and he died, aged 60, in 1957, believing himself forgotten. In recent years, however, his music has undergone a major revival, and 1997 marks the centenary year of his birth.

Violanta is set in sixteenth-century Venice, and tells the passionate story of a *grande dame* who plans to avenge the suicide of her sister, who was seduced and abandoned by Alfonso, the handsome Prince of Naples. Luring him to her bedroom, Violanta has instructed her husband to kill him upon a prearranged signal. But she herself falls in love with Alfonso, and when her husband appears, dagger drawn, she throws herself between them and dies instead.

Using a large orchestra, *Violanta* is an intense and highly erotic work, drenched in post-Straussian chromaticism, with that unique and personal use of bitonal harmony and voluptuous melodic writing which mark Korngold's highly individual style. What remains extraordinary is how the teenage composer, with no experience of sexual matters, was able to write such erotic music so convincingly. The opera culminates in a magnificent love duet guaranteed to make the spine tingle.

Introduced by Bruno Walter in Munich in 1916, *Violanta* provided the legendary diva Maria Jeritza with one of her most celebrated roles in Vienna and America, and together with its lighter companion work, *Der Ring des Polykrates*, was widely performed in Europe until 1933, though has been rarely heard since. This semi-staged production by Opera North marks the opera's London premiere, and is a fitting tribute to Korngold in his centenary year.

Opera North's semi-staging of Violanta *will be given in Prom 8. Korngold's Violin Concerto can be heard in Prom 22.*

Nation stakes

Calum MacDonald introduces Honegger's stage oratorio on Joan of Arc

THESE ARE dangerous times for national mythologies. I write as an English MP has suggested we boycott the Christmas mistletoe on sale in our shops: the British plant is failing and it's mostly now imported from France. With such attempts to widen the Channel, how will we receive a musical glorification of the life of France's national warrior-saint, culminating in her burning at the stake as a witch and heretic by the English in 1431 (not by the *British*, of course: the Scots fought on the French side)?

Yet the 'dramatic oratorio' *Joan of Arc at the Stake* was composed by a German-Swiss who was only an honorary Parisian, and the title-role for a Russian-Jewish actress and dancer. It was the last and grandest of Arthur Honegger's collaborations with Ida Rubinstein: when she played St Joan in Orleans, shortly before the outbreak of the Second World War, she provoked anti-Semitic attacks for daring to impersonate a pure Christian heroine. In fact, in so far as Honegger and his librettist, Paul Claudel, had a contemporary enemy in mind, it was Fascist repression – something made absolutely explicit in the Prologue they added after the Nazi occupation of France.

Contemptuous of artistic élitism and concerned to reach a wide audience, Honegger was forging a new kind of non-doctrinal religious choral work: *Joan of Arc* can be staged, semi-staged, or performed purely in concert, whether in an opera house, cathedral or concert hall. The scenic element remains implicit in the music whether or not it is enacted before the audience. Speaking actors counterpoint singers and choruses: the music is rich in detail and stylistic contrasts, yet the story line is strong, simple and compelling.

Honegger, composer of the express-train tone-poem *Pacific 231*, was deeply affected in his view of music's function by the technological advances of his age. None of these seemed more significant to him than the new mass medium of the cinema

Above Arthur Honegger (1892–1955)
Right Fiona Shaw
Below right Libor Pešek
Far right Joan of Arc at the Coronation of King Charles VII by Jean-Auguste Dominique Ingres

– he wrote over forty film scores, including the original music for Abel Gance's *Napoléon*. The first production of *Joan of Arc at the Stake* made use of film to illustrate the Dauphin's triumphant entry into Rheims, and the work as a whole is cinematically conceived, with its broad scenic effects, its tapestry-like colours, and the flashback technique of its narrative.

Claudel's sometimes too-clever text, with the action proceeding backwards in time, Joan's accusers turning into animals, and playing-cards into kings, has its difficulties. The mingling of speech and song always brings problems of its own, especially when the main character is relegated to a non-singing role. But the result is vivid, dramatic and undeniably touching. Honegger's music, for very large forces including two pianos and an ondes martenot (new technology again), has a staggering range of colour and invention, spanning Medievalism to jazz, and attaining tremendous power in the big choruses. Ultimately, this is a work whose greatness transcends frontiers.

Fiona Shaw stars as Joan of Arc in Deborah Warner's semi-staging of Honegger's work in Prom 11

EDINBURGH INTERNATIONAL FESTIVAL 50TH BIRTHDAY. MANY HAPPY RETURNS.

Registered Charity No. SC004694.

This year it's the Edinburgh Festival's 50th birthday. To celebrate we're recreating some of the great events and world premieres that have been the highlights of the last fifty years. Performances will include works by Tippett and Nono, and the original version of Strauss' Ariadne auf Naxos. Also returning will be some of the world's top conductors, like Boulez, Gergiev and Mackerras, and soloists like Bryn Terfel, Andras Schiff and Karita Mattila. As well, of course, as many other of the best known names in theatre, opera and dance. Edinburgh Festival's fiftieth birthday runs from 10th. August to 30th. August. Call 0131 473 2001 for your free brochure. (0131 473 2000 for the box office.)

Edinburgh
International FESTIVAL
50TH BIRTHDAY
1947 ~ 1997

EDINBURGH INTERNATIONAL FESTIVAL, 21 MARKET STREET, EDINBURGH EH1 1BW.

Burberrys

OF LONDON ®

For details of featured merchandise contact: The Wholesale Showroom, 165 Regent Street, London W1R 8AS. Telephone: 0171 734 5929

Please find below the list of all our retail stores within the U.K.

18-22 The Haymarket, London SW1Y 4DQ

165 Regent Street, London W1R 8AS

84-86 Regent Street, London W1R 5PF

2 Brompton Road, Knightsbridge, London SW1X 7PB

454-456 Union Street, Aberdeen AB1 1TR

39-41 Princes Street, Edinburgh EH2 2BY

64 Buchanan Street, Glasgow G1 3JE

51 Halkett Place, St. Helier, Jersey, C.I. JE2 4WG

Terminal 1, Heathrow Airport

Terminal 3, Heathrow Airport

FARRINGDONS

THE MUSIC STORE THAT KNOWS ABOUT MUSIC

Jazz

WORLD MUSIC

Classical

Soundtracks

Nostalgia

FARRINGDONS
PROMS VOUCHER

£2 *Off*

with this voucher on any CD over £14.49 when you visit a Farringdons Records Store or use our Mail Order Service

Name:

Address:

64-72 Leadenhall Market
London EC3V 1LT
Tel: 0171 623 9605

Royal Festival Hall
South Bank Centre
London SE1 8XX
Tel: 0171 620 0198

Mail Order Service:
0171 626 2805

Offer ends 30th Sept 1997

BBC

IF IT WEREN'T FOR THE BBC, THE LAST NIGHT OF THE PROMS WOULD HAVE BEEN ON THE

16TH OF OCTOBER, 1926.

SEVENTY years ago, the BBC came to the assistance of a popular but financially beleaguered classical music festival called the HENRY WOOD PROMENADE CONCERTS.

The festival has since flourished and grown to become the best known music festival in the world. THE PROMS, as they are now more affectionately known, have proved an excellent example of the BBC's commitment to music in Britain.

THIS year marks the 75th anniversary of the BBC. And throughout its 75 years, the unique way that the BBC has been funded by you, the British public, has ensured its continued support of all areas of British culture. THE BBC. YOU MAKE IT WHAT IT IS.

THE BRITISH BROADCASTING CORPORATION

New music from several generations of composers is featured this season, as **Adrian Jack** describes. Photographs by Malcolm Crowthers

AT THE AGE of seventy-five, Iannis Xenakis still presents one of the major musical challenges to audiences today. It is forty years since his first two works for orchestra, *Metastasis* and *Pithoprakta*, defined a new approach to a traditional institution, and pushed it into the front line of attack as a source of new sounds rivalling the fledgling medium of

we expect – there are pieces, for instance, with almost folksy characteristics. But he is an undeniably *big* creative personality, a beacon to musicians everywhere, and if in Britain we hear his large-scale pieces too rarely, there are a number of chamber and solo works that have acquired classic status.

Sir Peter Maxwell Davies is also one of the dominant musical figures of today and a charismatic personality who has always viewed his role as a member of a community. He first achieved fame,

New from old and young

electronic music. Xenakis has made electronic pieces too, and spectacular installations involving light and sound. His vision of music bypasses a conventional, purely 'musical' outlook, and accounts both for his unique contribution to composition in the second half of the twentieth century, and for his continuing status as a controversial figure.

Trained as an engineer and architect (he was Le Corbusier's assistant), his radical approach to organising sound is both intellectually appealing and emotionally compelling. Sometimes Xenakis is baffling, and sometimes, even, a new work by him surprises by not being as abstract or 'modern' as

around 1960, not just as a provocative and intellectually challenging young composer, but as a conspicuously successful schoolteacher and a motivator of boundless energy. When Davies went to live in Orkney in 1970 it was not to retreat from the world but to identify with a particular place. Not only did he start the St Magnus Festival in Kirkwall, but he also formed a close association both as composer and conductor with the Scottish Chamber Orchestra, for whom last year he completed his series of ten Strathclyde Concertos, conceived for particular members of the orchestra in turn, the final one being a concerto for the whole band.

Main picture left
Iannis Xenakis
Above
Sir Peter Maxwell Davies

From the very early days, Davies was highly conscious of tradition and particularly interested in Medieval music, while many of his more recent pieces have been concerned with Orkney history and customs. His Proms commission inaugurates a new series of fourteen works inspired by the eventful journey of Earl Rognvald II and Bishop William of Orkney to the Holy Land in 1151. It takes its title from the banners or 'sails' which were hung in the massive Romanesque bays of the nave in Kirkwall Cathedral during the 1993 St Magnus Festival. Each bore a caption by the Orkney poet George Mackay Brown, with whom Davies had a close working association, and who died in April 1996.

Jonathan Harvey is just five years younger than Davies and is one of several composers who seem to feel a need to reconcile technical innovation with an affirmation of spiritual values. He has developed a particular interest in combining live performance with electronics or tape, and his strong vein of Christian mysticism is clearly expressed in one of his best-known pieces, *Mortuos Plango, Vivos Voco*, an evocative transformation on tape of the voice of his son, then a choirboy at Winchester Cathedral, and the great tenor bell of the cathedral.

Bell sounds, or rather the spectral character of bells, will feature in his Percussion Concerto for Evelyn Glennie. Malletted

instruments will be dominant, particularly the marimba, rather than instruments of indefinite pitch. Harvey describes the first movement as 'contrapuntal, Bachian and waltzy'. The slow middle movement, by contrast, will be 'sensuous,

blurred and coloured'. And in the perpetual motion of the finale, 'the entire Universe vibrates', like the light on the Pacific coast of California, where the composer is permanent part-time Professor at Stanford.

One of the youngest composers represented in this year's Proms is thirty-five-year-old David Sawer, who in the last few years has produced a succession of major pieces which are both impressively inventive and finely crafted. He came of age musically while still, for a composer, very young, with *Cat's-Eye* ten years ago. His first Proms commission, *Byrnan Wood*, composed for the 1992 season, was also Sawer's first big orchestral work. Last year his Trumpet Concerto, commissioned by the soloist Graham Ashton, was played at the Royal Festival Hall by the BBC Symphony Orchestra, and earlier this year the London Sinfonietta gave the first performance of *Tiroirs*.

Byrnan Wood was a study in the subtle art of musical camouflage, but Sawer says the new piece will be very transparent, light and airy. Its title, *the greatest happiness principle*, comes from the philosophy of Jeremy Bentham, who did so much to influence nineteenth-century penal and welfare reform. How this will relate to Sawer's music remains to be heard; Bentham's ideas have been identified as the sources of laissez-faire capitalism on the one hand and totalitarianism on the other but

Top
Jonathan Harvey
Bottom
David Sawer

Sawer sees a connection between social accountability and musical integrity, whereby something simple grows organically, rather than being governed by a preconceived scheme.

Of the same generation, Magnus Lindberg (born 1958) is one of the best-known younger Finnish composers. Outside his own country he has a strong reputation in Germany and France, and he has become quite familiar in Britain, having been featured composer at the Aldeburgh Festival in 1995 and Artistic Director of 'Meltdown' on the South Bank last summer. The BBC commissioned Lindberg's *Corrente II*, first performed by the BBC Symphony Orchestra, in 1992, and the London Sinfonietta has programmed several of Lindberg's works, jointly commissioning *Engine* last year with the Aldeburgh Festival and the South Bank Centre. It is an apt title for music which is hotly dynamic though never mechanical. A former pupil of the French composer Gérard Grisey, Lindberg has developed and enriched his teacher's way of exploring the harmonic spectrum with his own powerful sense of organic continuity.

One of European music's most respected senior figures, Hans Werner Henze has said that in all his work the old forms 'strive to regain significance, even when the modern timbre of the music seldom or never allows them to appear on the surface'. Henze made his mark early on in the opera house, and in

Top
Magnus Lindberg
Centre
Mark-Anthony Turnage
Bottom
Hans Werner Henze

January this year his latest stage-piece, *Venus and Adonis*, was given its first performance by the Bavarian State Opera. As founder of a music theatre festival in Munich, Henze has also been an important influence in bringing other, younger composers' work to fruition. His enormous output includes every genre; but drama, and words, fired for a considerable period by political concerns, have been at the heart of his music. It is not often abstract, or rarely feels it. On the contrary, it can be extravagantly expressive. His lush Eighth Symphony, performed at the 1995 Proms, has a Shakespearean programme.

Henze's connection with the Proms has always been close, and it was at the Proms in 1993 that he heard the Leipzig Gewandhaus Orchestra live for the first time. They played Bruckner's Fourth Symphony under Kurt Masur, and Henze was enormously impressed, especially by the strings. He says he wanted to explore further the kind of vocal music he was then writing for six *a cappella* 'madrigal-singers' in *Venus and Adonis*, but in instrumental terms. The result, his Second Sonata for Strings, is richly-textured melodic music, with two slow movements framing a lighter, faster one. The Leipzig Gewandhaus Orchestra gave the first performance last November.

Seven years ago, Henze pupil and Essex boy Mark-Anthony Turnage reached television audiences with his Oedipal opera of present-day domestic horrors, *Greek*. Turnage is now Composer in Residence with English National Opera, for whom he is writing a work planned for 1999. *Dispelling the Fears*, originally written for the Philharmonia Orchestra in 1995, is played at the Proms by the BBC Symphony Orchestra conducted by Oliver Knussen (another of Turnage's teachers) and features taxing and very persistent parts for two solo trumpets, which intertwine as one instrument. The title describes how an atmosphere of

glowering threat is eventually dispelled in a serene ending.

Ligeti traces the ancestry of his six *Nonsense Madrigals* back still further than Henze. On the one hand, he says, he's found inspiration for these short but intense pieces – commissioned and performed by the King's Singers – in the intricate music of Europe in the fourteenth century, and on the other, in the timeless rhythmic traditions of Africa. Ligeti has written these, like a good many of his works, over a number of years – the last was added in 1993. Humour, or rather a kind of craziness, has always been prominent in his musical makeup. *Aventures* and *Nouvelles Aventures*, then much later, his opera *Le Grand Macabre*, showed his taste for the bizarre and an inventive use of voices beyond singing in the conventional sense. But the *Madrigals* require precise pitching, because they have quite clear tonal harmonies, though often in unexpected contexts, which make faking on the part of singers impossible. Their difficulties are wickedly exposed, and all the more exciting for it. Ligeti's humour should be all too clear to Proms audiences, because it has a decidedly British bias, and the *Madrigals* include several settings of Lewis Carroll, one of Ligeti's favourite authors.

Born in the Tatar Republic in 1931, Sofia Gubaidulina belongs to the same generation as Alfred

Schnittke and the late Edison Denisov – the same generation, too, as our own Maxwell Davies and Sir Harrison Birtwistle. Like Schnittke, she now lives in North Germany. Gubaidulina only began to be heard with any frequency in Britain after *glasnost* – neither her concern with spiritual values nor her interest in new musical techniques endeared her to Soviet officialdom before that. The impulse behind her music is nearly always literary, whether she sets a text or not, and she has strong religious leanings which can only have been strengthened by years of official disapproval.

One of Gubaidulina's first big works to make a strong impression here was her Violin Concerto, *Offertorium*, begun in 1980, the final version of which Gidon Kremer played with the BBC Symphony Orchestra in London in 1986 and with the CBSO at the Proms in 1991. In a comparable way to Schnittke, Gubaidulina relates contemporary methods to the distant past: in *Offertorium* she takes a theme from Bach's *Musical Offering* as a series which is treated rather in the manner of Webern. Gubaidulina wrote her Viola Concerto for Yuri Bashmet and the Chicago Symphony Orchestra, who gave the first performance earlier this year.

The Scottish composer Edward McGuire, who is now in his late forties, revisits the past in terms unmistakably of today in his

Top left
Sofia Gubaidulina
Bottom left
György Ligeti
Right Edward McGuire
Bottom right
Tristan Keuris

turbulently atmospheric tone-poem *Calgacus*. The title is the name of the Pictish leader who was defeated at Mons Graupius by the Romans under Agricola in 84 AD, and whose speech of reproach ('You have created a desert and called it peace') was recorded by Tacitus. McGuire plays flute with the Scottish traditional folk group The Whistle-binkies – the first such group to tour China, in 1992 – and he frequently incorporates national idioms in his music. *Calgacus* climaxes defiantly, poignantly, with the sound of bagpipes, which are gradually engulfed and swept away by a wave of fierce orchestral dissonance, leaving a haunting, pacific, but almost interrogative ending.

Finally, on a slightly sad note, the Royal Concertgebouw Orchestra from Amsterdam introduce Three Preludes to this country by way of a tribute to one of Holland's most respected composers, Tristan Keuris, who died last December at the age of fifty. He completed Three Preludes in 1994, shortly before writing his Symphony in D, a bold and unexpectedly classical title for a present-day composer, but one which proclaimed Keuris's growing regard for traditional forms.

Royal Philharmonic
Britain's and Classic FM's
national orchestra

The Royal Philharmonic Orchestra in London

Royal Albert Hall & Barbican Centre

Highlights for 1997/8

Tchaikovsky *Complete Symphony Cycle*
WITH MUSIC DIRECTOR DANIELE GATTI

Bartók *Piano Concertos*
WITH PETER DONOHOE

Brahms *German Requiem*

Orff *Carmina Burana*

Prokofiev *Alexander Nevsky*

"The Royal Philharmonic
Orchestra is playing with a
new confidence that bodes
well for the future"
THE TIMES

The Royal Philharmonic Orchestra – with residencies at the Royal Albert Hall and Nottingham

Please send me details of concerts by the Royal Philharmonic Orchestra

Name ....

Address ....

....

.... Postcode ....

Send to Royal Philharmonic Orchestra, FREEPOST, London ECIB IRP

jamin Britten Ralph Vaughan Williams William Walton Eleanor Alberga
erald Barry Michael Berkeley John Buller Martin Butler Andrew Carter
Gordon Crosse Michael Finnissy Roberto Gerhard Edward Harper Alun
ddinott Constant Lambert Libby Larsen William Mathias Elis Pehkonen
rald Plain Anthony Powers Alan Rawsthorne John Rutter Robert Sherla
Johnson Howard Skempton Hilary Tann Phyllis Tate David Willcocks
njamin Britten Ralph Vaughan Williams William Walton Eleanor Alberga
erald Barry Michael Berkeley John Buller Martin Butler Andrew Carter
Gordon Crosse Michael Finnissy Roberto Gerhard Edward Harper Alun
ddinott Constant Lambert Libby Larsen William Mathias Elis Pehkonen
rald Plain Anthony Powers Alan Rawsthorne John Rutter Robert Sherla
Johnson Howard Skempton Hilary Tann Phyllis Tate David Willcocks
njamin Britten Ralph Vaughan Williams William Walton Eleanor Alberga
erald Barry Michael Berkeley John Buller Martin Butler Andrew Carter
Gordon Crosse Michael Finnissy Roberto Gerhard Edward Harper Alun
ddinott Constant Lambert Libby Larsen William Mathias Elis Pehkonen
rald Plain Anthony Powers Alan Rawsthorne John Rutter Robert Sherla

Oxford

composer

Repertoire Promotions, Oxford University Press, 70 Barker Street, London W1M 1DJ
Telephone 0171 616 5900, Facsimile 0171 616 5901, E-mail repertoire.promotion@oup.co.uk

Johns   cocks
njamin Britten Ralph Vaughan Williams William Walton Eleanor Alberga
erald Barry Michael Berkeley John Buller Martin Butler Andrew Carter

Even experts need frequent re-tuning.

Vital network

In the year that the Association of British Orchestras celebrates its golden jubilee, **Nick Kimberley** assesses the strength of our orchestral life

CLASSICAL MUSIC is in crisis. Too many orchestras compete for an audience that is not only diminishing, but is getting older at a rapid rate. They are a drain on dwindling resources, and there isn't enough talent to go round. Here is one commentator looking back over the previous year: 'Orchestras were so numerous ... that they strained the supply of possible names as well as of competent players; the conducting profession was busier than ever; and in the general hustle the quality of performance continued to descend'.

Sounds familiar? Well, that was 1946, dimly viewed in W. McNaught's 'London Letter', published in *The Chesterian* in 1947. Classical music managed to weather that crisis, and the intervening half-century has been something of a golden age for orchestras in Britain. It was in 1947 that the Association of British Orchestras (ABO) was founded at the instigation of the newly born Arts Council, as a lobbying and negotiating body charged with overseeing orchestral life. Fifty years later, as the ABO celebrates its golden jubilee, its membership includes over sixty orchestras.

The ABO's present director, Libby MacNamara, points out that the Berlin Philharmonic receives more in public funding than all of Britain's orchestras put together, and that, far from Britain being swamped with orchestras, there are fewer per head of population than in Germany, France or Sweden. MacNamara admits, 'Yes, there has been a falling-off of audience numbers over the past five years, which has coincided with an appalling recession, but we're beginning to see some growth in audiences throughout the country. People say that it's an ageing audience, but it was ageing when I was young, and yet it keeps replenishing itself'.

The Proms continue to give an overview of the breadth and variety of orchestral life in Britain and the orchestras run and funded by the BBC, as ever, play a central role. Whether playing old music on period instruments, or performing new scores on which the ink is barely dry, each ensemble has developed its own survival mechanisms for the twenty-first century. Whereas in 1947 the life of an orchestra might be defined almost exclusively in terms of the concert hall, the pre-millennial orchestra leads a more varied life. John Bimson is Chairman of the Board of Directors of the Royal Philharmonic Orchestra (RPO). He is also the orchestra's principal horn player. In his view, 'If orchestras stay as we are, we become dinosaurs, and will go the way of the dinosaurs. There are ways of communicating that aren't about sitting on the concert platform in penguin suits'.

For the RPO, founded in 1946, the search for new ways of communicating involves looking beyond London, its traditional base: besides a Royal Albert Hall residency, it has a second 'home' in Nottingham's Royal Concert Hall

Illustration by Simon Stern

where, as Bimson notes with some pride, 'Our residency is in its third year, and it's been a tremendous success. Audiences have grown, we've really got to know the people, and we've played in jails, hospitals, factory canteens, shops and drug rehabilitation centres. The players are absolutely committed to it: they've been educated in how to educate'.

Bimson's view is echoed by Malcolm Stewart, leader of the Royal Liverpool Philharmonic Orchestra (RLPO): 'Everyone in the orchestra understands that educational and outreach work is part of the job. It's here to stay. The next generation of listeners has to have doors opened for them, and if that means us going out to them rather than them coming to us, as they used to, then it has to be done. There is a huge question-mark over the cultural development of the next generation, on which we will depend in years to come, and I worry for the future'.

For the Scottish Chamber Orchestra (SCO), outreach work can find the players covering vast distances, working anywhere between the Borders and Orkney. 'The SCO', says Managing Director Roy McEwan, 'is very much one of the Scottish national orchestras, serving the whole of Scotland in a variety of ways. The orchestra's flexibility is one of its great strengths. In any given year we undertake something like 300 small projects, and perhaps forty larger projects. That involves huge numbers of people, and we see it as a long-term development exercise, but it is also an experience in itself. Whoever the project is for, that's the musical experience they're having, and it's as valid as walking into a concert hall.'

The modern orchestra, then, feels as much at home outside as inside the concert hall. And there is another location each has made its own: the recording studio. Far from rendering concert-hall orchestras irrelevant, recording itself relies on their existence. Few orchestras record as prolifically as the RPO, which with one company alone has recorded The Royal Philharmonic Collection of 100 CDs in barely three years. That is a phenomenal work-rate on top of live performances, but as John Bimson says, 'We could never simply be a recording orchestra. Our *raison d'être* is to play to people. That's why I sit and practise Mahler for hours on end, not to play it chunk by chunk in the studio'.

No orchestra, though, can afford to underestimate the importance of recordings, and not only as a source of income. Tony Woodcock is Managing Director of the Bournemouth Symphony Orchestra and of its junior partner, the Bournemouth Sinfonietta, both frequently recorded. As Woodcock puts it, 'If you don't have recordings, you don't have a calling-card'. That is essential if an orchestra is to reach an international audience. Woodcock insists that a strong regional identity does not mean his orchestras are parochial: 'Our region covers nine counties, for which we provide the major pillar of professional music-making, in terms of concerts and of community or education work. Without us, a population of around seven million people would be deprived of live orchestral music. But I'm proud to say that both orchestras have a national and international identity: last year we played at the Musikverein in Vienna and at the Concertgebouw in Amsterdam, and this April we make our debut in Carnegie Hall'.

Those sentiments are echoed by Simon Clugston, founder and now Artistic Director of the Birmingham Contemporary Music Group (BCMG): 'We're fiercely proud of what we do in Birmingham, and think that the musical life being created here is unparalleled in this country, but we're not at all "provincial" about it. We have played all over the world, and expect the highest standards from our players'. As its name implies, the BCMG (formed by players from the City of Birmingham Symphony Orchestra) exists to perform the music of our own time: in the decade since its formation it has premiered some thirty new works, many commissioned with funds generated by its Sound

NGLISH NORTHERN PHILHARMONIA

BBC
Symphony
Orchestra

Investment scheme, which encourages audience members to buy a stake in the piece. For Clugston, 'The Sound Investment initiative has a fund-raising function, but more importantly, it involves the audience in the creative process. By the time a piece is premiered, those who have invested have gone to the first rehearsal, met the composer, seen the work build, and they feel very protective towards it'.

It is sometimes suggested that an orchestra's commitment to new work extends no further than a first performance, but that is not BCMG's way. 'We don't do one-off premieres. We have a policy that any new work has to be repeated within two years of its first performance, and some pieces are heard a lot more. We've performed Mark-Anthony Turnage's *Kai*, for instance, around twenty times. And no less important is that the pieces are performed elsewhere in the world by other ensembles.'

Paul Daniel, soon to take up the post of Music Director at English National Opera, but currently Music Director of Opera North and Principal Conductor of its orchestra, the English Northern Philharmonia, also pays more than lip service to new work. When, four years ago, he won a Prudential Award, he put the prize money towards a new commission for the orchestra, which, he says, 'has a strong relationship with contemporary music, and plays

it very well. In recent years at Opera North we've premiered operas by Robert Saxton, Michael Berkeley and Benedict Mason. I firmly believe that we must pay all due respect to the artists working within our culture'.

For Daniel the English Northern Philharmonia's dual identity as an orchestra for the opera house and for the concert hall gives it a special quality. 'When you play in the opera house pit, you have to be good accompanists. That stands you in good stead on the concert platform where, if you like, the players are accompanying each other: one of the prides of this orchestra is to be able to produce a real *pianissimo*, which is quite rare these days. It's an orchestra which strongly identifies with its community, as many regional orchestras do, and that's something the London orchestras would love to have. Our support is loyal, prepared to make experiments with you in unusual repertoire, the kind of thing that audiences in the metropolis might think twice about attending.'

Daniel's orchestra is one of six that have formed the Northern Orchestra Consortium: the others are the Royal Liverpool Philharmonic, Newcastle's Northern Sinfonia, and three from Manchester, the Hallé Orchestra, the BBC Philharmonic and the Manchester Camerata. As the RLPO's leader Malcolm Stewart suggests, 'The idea is to work

together, rather than in opposition, to enhance the quality of orchestral music in the North.

So while orchestras assert their own identity, they're also aware of the need to co-operate. The need is all the more pressing in Manchester, with its three professional orchestras. But John Whibley of the Hallé refutes any suggestion that three is a crowd: 'Manchester certainly needs all these orchestras. I don't see us as being in competition: we're all working hard, playing a wide range of repertoire to very good audiences. Within one hour's drive of Bridgewater Hall, which is our new home, we have eight million people, and if Manchester is to be an important musical centre, we need a vibrant musical life'.

The same, of course, needs to be said about the country as a whole. No orchestra has a divine right to exist, and the funding crisis faced by so many has at least made them aware of their mortality, as the ABO's Libby MacNamara suggests: 'Orchestras in this country have had to evolve very quickly in the harsh climate of the last decade or so. They're not complacent, they're responding to the needs of the audience, in and out of the concert hall. There is a genuine desire to reinvigorate the concert experience'. Perhaps the real question is whether audiences, as much a part of the concert experience as the orchestras, can prove themselves as capable of adapting. That responsibility is ours.

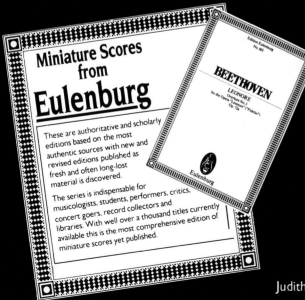

Royal Festival Hall
on the South Bank

sbc

London Philharmonic Orchestra
Resident at the Royal Festival Hall

Philharmonia Orchestra
Associate orchestra of the Royal Festival Hall

Orchestra of the Age of Enlightenment
Associate orchestra of the Royal Festival Hall

London Sinfonietta
Associate of the Royal Festival Hall

Alban Berg Quartet
Associate artists of the Royal Festival Hall

For booking and information on forthcoming concerts by all of our associates call the Royal Festival Hall Box Office on **0171 960 4242**.

TRINITY
college of music:

Patron: HRH The Duke of Kent KG. Principal: Gavin Henderson

Trinity, with a long and innovative tradition of performance-based training, prepares students for a professional career in music

- High quality individual tuition. Performance of contemporary and unusual works alongside the standard repertoire.

- 4-year BMus (TCM) 'Music Plus' degree*

- MA (Music Education)*

- MMus in Performance Studies**
  (a new degree beginning in September 1997)

- PG Certificate

* Validated by the University of Westminster
** Validated by the University of Sussex

Trinity College of Music
Mandeville Place
London W1M 6AQ
Telephone: 0171. 935 5773
Facsimile: 0171. 224 6278

Registered Charity No. 309998

WE'RE PLEASED TO HAVE BEEN ABLE TO HELP THE BBC PROMS SET THE BALL ROLLING.

CAMELOT

BRINGING YOU THE WORLD'S LEADING LOTTERY

THE PROMS SPREADS its wings this summer from one great Victorian building to another. Proms Chamber Music is moving to the Victoria and Albert Museum – a vast treasure-house of art, craft and design, reflecting every civilisation, style and subject. Go up the Ceramic Staircase and through the glittering, newly-refurbished Silver Galleries, and you come to the Lecture Theatre – a spacious auditorium seating three hundred, with a stage surmounted by a lavishly-decorated apse featuring allegories of Art, Poetry, Science and Philosophy. Grandeur was the order of the day when they built the Victoria and Albert Museum and the Royal Albert Hall.

Left
The Victoria and Albert Museum

Right
The Lecture Theatre

soirée that the Proms Chamber Music will be re-creating this year on 25 August. This is the day that Glyndebourne comes to the Proms with Rossini's *Count Ory* – an opera written for Paris where Rossini settled for the final years of his life and played host at a brilliant succession of Saturday Evening concerts. These attracted the cream of musicians from all over Europe, including Liszt, who gave the first performance of his *Legends*.

Picking up on links like that, and to complement the main season of concerts, is how Proms Chamber Music came into being last season. This year the chamber concerts celebrate the anniversaries of Schubert with his radiant String Quintet, and Brahms with his exhilarating Variations and Fugue on a Theme by Handel. Arvo Pärt

new work by Christopher Fox on texts from the revolutionary years of seventeenth-century England. There is also the London premiere of a new piano piece by Stephen Montague, inspired by the music of the American Deep South. And the concerts present in a more intimate setting some of the artists also appearing in the main Proms – pianist Stephen Kovacevich, soprano Joan Rodgers, and an ensemble of flute, viola and harp from the visiting Royal Concertgebouw Orchestra.

Music among the decorative arts of the V&A means the enjoyment of new ventures and new discoveries. It's what Proms Chamber Music is all about!

Intimate grandeur

Edward Blakeman introduces the Proms Chamber Music Series

But musical grandeur comes in many shapes and sizes – it's not just big orchestras. The first Prom, for example, back in 1895 was a very mixed bag, with five solo singers and three solo instrumentalists. The whole thing must have had a distinct air of drawing-room *soirée* writ large. Maybe it was not unlike the sort of

and Percy Grainger rub shoulders with mingled resonances of sacred liturgy and secular folk song, while Britten and Bartók – two featured Proms composers – are paired in two masterly string quartets. Voices and viols separately explore ancient and modern settings of Alleluias and In Nomines, and combine for a vivid

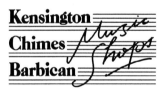

Jaques Samuel
PIANOS

Winner of the *Best Retailer of the Year 1996 - MIA*
Sponsors of the **1996/97 Gramophone Instrumental** Award

C.BECHSTEIN

STEINWAY & SONS

Bösendorfer

"Claudio Arrau, my beloved teacher and mentor always urged us to coax sound, colour, character and personality from the piano on which we **had** to perform."

"You have a choice of the *finest* at Jaques Samuel Pianos, and I promise you, your choice will be the beginning of a wonderful love affair!"

Ruth Nye
Professor of Piano,
Yehudi Menuhin School

For Further information please return this coupon to Bechstein House

☐ Bechstein Pianos	Name
☐ Bösendorfer Pianos	School or Institution
☐ Steinway Pianos	Address
☐ Hire/Tuning Services	
☐ Refurbishment Services	
☐ Forthcoming Events	Telephone Number

Jaques Samuel Pianos Ltd

Bechstein House, 142 Edgware Road, Marble Arch, London, W2 2DZ   Tel 0171 723 8818   Fax 0171 224 8692
The Steinway Pianos offered are restored to the highest standards in our own factory, using the finest German materials

Standing up

Edward Bhesania
explains the fun of Promming

for music

THE PROMS ARE envied the world over for their unique and informal atmosphere – somehow the expectant murmurs from the audience seem that much more animated, the settling hush before the start that much more dramatic than at other concerts.

Especially so, perhaps, when standing in the Arena at the centre of the hall's imposing rotunda. From this position, as well as feeling more closely connected with the action on-stage, it's possible to enjoy an even clearer orchestral balance than in the stalls: ironically, for the distinctly unprincely sum of £3, you get the best 'seats' in the house. But you don't always have to listen on your legs. For all but the most popular concerts there's usually enough room to sit down, or even lie back on the floor, and early birds in the Arena can vie for the seats circling the central fountain.

If you're after an impressive aerial view of the proceedings, you can choose to Prom in the spacious Gallery circling the top of the auditorium. 'It's cooler, and the people are nicer', suggests one Prommer with a clear preference for the hall's uppermost regions. As another Gallery regular describes it, 'The sound rises, the view of the orchestra is superb, the atmosphere is terrific and generally it gives you a tremendous amount of happiness'.

Another major attraction of Promming is the price. For a fraction of the cost of other concert tickets you can hear the world's leading soloists, conductors and orchestras, offering an inexpensive opportunity to sample a huge range of music, and encouraging an adventurous approach to the new or the unknown. Countless musicians and music lovers have found their orchestral favourites this way, often when least expected. 'The concerts that really struck me last year,' said one enthusiast, 'were those which I initially thought might not really be my kind of thing.'

A further benefit is flexibility. Since Arena and Gallery tickets for individual concerts are not booked in advance, the number of people in your party doesn't have to be fixed ahead of the event, and you can almost be guaranteed entrance to concerts which may otherwise have sold out weeks in advance. Central to the whole experience is the

friendly atmosphere of the Proms queue: it's the ideal place to arrange to meet friends – and make new ones – and there's always the

Points for Prommers
• Doors open around an hour before the performance.

• For most concerts it's safe to arrive one or two hours before the start, but queues tend to form earlier in the afternoon for star performers and orchestras.

• If you want a position at the front of the Arena (not necessarily the best place acoustically) you'll need to arrive earlier.

• Entrance to the Hall for Arena Prommers is by Door 2, but the queue starts opposite Doors 13/14, at a lamp post at the top of the steps leading to Prince Consort Road – an elegant setting between the impressive Hall itself and the Royal College of Music.

• Gallery Prommers enter by Door 10. This queue starts at the next lamp post along, extending down Bremner Road.

chance of catching some summer sun before the concert.

Promming also provides a first-hand impression (if not a guaranteed understanding) of the distinctive humour which, during its brief moments, puts the Prommers centre-stage. As concert-going becomes increasingly less formal, remember – the Proms got there first!

Don't worry if you can't make it

BBC RADIO 3

Radio 3 Presenter
Stephanie Hughes

Around the Proms on BBC Radio 3

Radio 3 brings you the complete Proms season wherever you are, with every concert broadcast live, and, for the first time this year, Proms will be repeated regularly on Wednesday afternoons: see *Radio Times* for full details. There are also six live relays on BBC2 Television, including the First and Last Nights, and four recorded Proms on BBC1. Radio 3 also takes you around the Proms with special programmes and series designed to add background and enhance your enjoyment of the season.

Proms Intervals

Many aspects of the Proms season will be explored in the Intervals to the live concerts, from introductions to significant or newly commissioned works, to celebratory features for the anniversaries of Schubert, Brahms and Mendelssohn, and portraits of some of the visiting orchestras and Radio 3 Proms Artists of the Week.

Proms News

The lively weekly magazine programme *Proms News*, presented by Stephen Johnson, will highlight main events and survey the concerts, including interviews with major artists and up-to-the-minute information as the season unfolds (**Saturdays, 9.00am, repeated Sundays, 30 minutes before the start of the evening's Proms**)

Proms Documentaries

A major series of in-depth documentaries on **Saturdays at 5.45pm** during the season gives you a chance to focus on composers featured in this year's Proms, including Lou Harrison, John Adams, Roy Harris, Iannis Xenakis, and Erich Wolfgang Korngold.

Proms Artist of the Week

Some of the big names performing at the Proms will be featured as Proms Artists of the Week in two of Radio 3's regular programmes: *Brian Kay's Sunday Morning* **(Sundays, 9.00am–12.30pm)** and *Musical Encounters* **(Weekdays, 10.00am–12.00 noon)**.

Nicholas McGegan	**13–18 July**
Stephen Kovacevich	**20–25 July**
The King's Singers	**27 July–1 August**
Luba Orgonasova	**3–8 August**
Christian Tetzlaff	**10–15 August**
Thomas Hampson	**17–22 August**
Roger Norrington	**24–29 August**
Louis Lortie	**31 August–5 September**
Maxim Vengerov	**7–12 September**

Proms Composer of the Week

During the Proms, the ever-popular *Composer of the Week* **(weekdays at 12.00 noon, repeated the next week at 11.30pm, 12.00 midnight on Fridays)** will celebrate composer anniversaries and complement some of the major themes in the Proms:

Beethoven	**14–18 July**
John Adams	**21–25 July**
Honegger	**28 July–1 August**
Brahms	**4–8 August**
Bartók	**11–15 August**
Britten	**18–22 August**
Mendelssohn	**25–29 August**
Schubert	**1–5 September**
Verdi	**8–12 September**

476 entrants.
56 countries.
42 composers.
2 conductors.
52 strings.
18 brass.
16 woodwind.
25 competitors.
5 finalists.
7 judges.
1 sponsor.

**All together now, it's the
1997 Cardiff Singer of the World Competition.**

1997 Cardiff Singer of the World Competition

Concert rounds 15th - 19th June. Final: Saturday 21st June. St David's Hall, The Hayes, Cardiff. Tel: 01222 878437
Rounds broadcast nightly on BBC2 during week commencing Monday 16th June. Final live on BBC2 and Radio3.

Winners' Concert 7.30pm, Wednesday 25th June Barbican Concert Hall, Silk Street, London EC2. Tel: 0171 638 8891

Understanding the Booking Section

This section of the Proms Guide gives full details of all the concerts on offer in the 1997 season with information on how to book tickets for your chosen performances.

We start with an **index** of where to find the relevant pieces of information, plus a guide to the **symbols** used. Full **concert details** are then listed, followed by information on **Proms Chamber Music, Promming, Same Day Savers, Group Bookings, Premiere Nights** – and how to get tickets for the **Last Night**.

The next few pages take you through **the booking process** – when to book, where to sit and how to pay. And finally we give **information on the Royal Albert Hall and information for people with special needs**, plus a detailed **index of artists** appearing **and works to be performed**.

Points to help you get the tickets of your choice

The 1996 Proms saw a record number of tickets purchased, with average attendance across the season at almost 90%. On the date that priority booking opened, the Royal Albert Hall received 15,000 forms; so inevitably some people were unable to secure tickets for the concerts of their choice.

To help ensure that you *do* receive the tickets that you want, please bear in mind the following:

- Try to take advantage of our priority booking period. Full details of when to book appear on page 124.

- Some patrons who booked only for concerts in price codes B or C were disappointed last year. Remember that if you book tickets for a concert in price codes B or C, priority will be given to your application if you also book at least one concert from price code A. Full details appear on page 124.

Important dates
Wednesday 21 May Priority postal and fax booking opens
Monday 16 June Telephone and personal booking opens

Phone and fax numbers
0171 589 8212 (telephone) **0171 225 0439** (fax)
Royal Albert Hall Ticket Shop

Contents

Index

Explaining our symbols

To simplify booking, the following symbols have been used above each concert listing:

Each concert in the Proms season has its own performance number. This helps avoid confusion when there is more than one concert on a particular date.

Denotes a concert with a premiere where a special discount applies. Please see page 122.

'Same-Day Saver' Tickets allow a discount on some afternoon and late-night concerts provided purchase is combined with the main evening concert. See page 123.

You can write to the Proms at:
BBC Proms, Broadcasting House, London W1A 1AA

or send an e-mail to:
Proms@bbc.co.uk

Visit the Proms site on the internet at:
http://www.bbc.co.uk/proms/

Prom 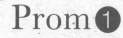 1

Friday 18 July
7.30pm – c9.05pm
Price Code B

Beethoven
Missa Solemnis   83'

Karita Mattila soprano
Catherine Wyn-Rogers
mezzo-soprano
Kurt Streit tenor
Anthony Michaels-Moore
baritone

BBC Singers
BBC Symphony Chorus
BBC Symphony Orchestra
Bernard Haitink conductor

'From the heart: may it reach the heart': Beethoven's dedication of his heaven-storming Mass setting shows that it is at once a grandly universal and an intimately personal statement of his beliefs. Bernard Haitink makes a welcome return to the BBC Symphony Orchestra with outstanding soloists to inaugurate the season; later there are Masses by J. S. Bach, Schubert and Verdi. It also begins a series of works threaded through the 1997 Proms that the composer Johannes Brahms conducted in his concerts in Vienna.

Commentary by Nicholas Kenyon and Stephen Maddock

Prom 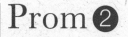 2

Saturday 19 July
7.30pm – c9.40pm
Price Code A

Mozart
Overture
'The Marriage of Figaro'   4'

Ah, lo previdi   12'

Chi sà, chi sà, qual sia   3'

Chaconne from 'Idomeneo'   12'

I N T E R V A L

Schubert
Die Verschworenen   60'

Countess Ludmilla
    Hillevi Martinpelto soprano
Count Heribert
    David Wilson-Johnson baritone
Astolf **Jamie MacDougall** tenor
Helene   **Lisa Larsson** soprano
Udolin
    Susan Bickley mezzo-soprano
Isella **Judith Howarth** soprano

Choir of the Enlightenment
Orchestra of the Age of
Enlightenment
Nicholas McGegan conductor

Sparkling music by Mozart leads to a witty, lyrical Schubert rarity for his bicentenary, a drama of domestic conflict in the Crusades which is the most successful of all his neglected operas.

Prom  3

Sunday 20 July
7.30pm – c9.55pm
Price Code A

Steve Reich
Music for Mallet Instruments,
Voices and Organ   16'

Michael Gordon
New work   c10'
BBC commission: world premiere

Lou Harrison
Concerto for Organ and Percussion
UK premiere   23'

I N T E R V A L

John Adams
Scratchband   15'
UK premiere

Philip Glass
Façades   7'

Frank Zappa
The Yellow Shark – excerpts   18'

Hermann Kretzschmar organ

Ensemble Modern
John Adams conductor

John Adams, fifty this year, meets Frank Zappa, old rivals Philip Glass and Steve Reich, and eighty-year-old Lou Harrison for a noisy birthday bash.

Pre-Prom Talk at 6.15pm: see p139
John Adams and Michael Gordon

Prom 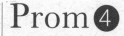 4

Monday 21 July
7.30pm – c9.50pm
Price Code A

Bach
Cantata No. 214
'Tönet ihr Pauken'   26'

Brandenburg Concerto No 4
in G major   15'

I N T E R V A L

Bach
Motet 'Jesu meine Freude'   19'

Cantata No. 21 'Ich hatte viel
Bekümmernis'   37'

Sibylla Rubens soprano
Elisabeth von Magnus alto
Mark Padmore tenor
Klaus Mertens bass

Amsterdam Baroque Choir
Amsterdam Baroque Orchestra
Ton Koopman conductor

A wide-ranging portrait of Bach's genius from one of the leading Bach conductors of our time: the exuberant Cantata No. 214 contains music from the *Christmas Oratorio*, and the deeply-felt Cantata No. 21 was conducted by Brahms in the nineteenth century.

Chamber Music at 1.00pm: see p118

Prom ⑤

Tuesday 22 July
7.30pm – c9.45pm
Price Code A

Mendelssohn
Overture 'Ruy Blas'   8'

Elgar
Cello Concerto in E minor   29'

I N T E R V A L

Bruckner
Symphony No. 9 in D minor   60'

Steven Isserlis cello

BBC National Orchestra of Wales
Tadaaki Otaka conductor

Bruckner's great unfinished symphony, one of his most powerful creations, is mirrored by the elegiac concerto which was the last masterpiece Elgar wrote before a decade of near-silence. The Conductor Laureate of the BBC National Orchestra of Wales – and a firm Proms favourite – Tadaaki Otaka, prefaces these two dark masterpieces with a lighter tribute to another of this year's anniversary composers, Felix Mendelssohn, who died 150 years ago.

Prom ⑥ ↗

Wednesday 23 July
7.00pm – c9.05pm
Price Code A

Iannis Xenakis
SEA-CHANGE   c10'
BBC commission: world premiere

Prokofiev
Piano Concerto No. 3
in C major   30'

I N T E R V A L

Strauss
Ein Heldenleben   45'

John Lill piano

BBC Symphony Orchestra
Andrew Davis conductor

Richard Strauss's rhapsodic portrait of a hero's life is the choice of the Chief Conductor of the BBC Symphony Orchestra in a typically bold programme, which draws together the warmth of Strauss with the sharp-edged clarity of Prokofiev, and introduces the first of the season's Proms commissions from one of the most original of contemporary composers, Iannis Xenakis, seventy-five this year.

Pre-Prom Talk at 5.45pm: see p139
Iannis Xenakis

Prom ⑦ ↗

Wednesday 23 July
10.00pm – c11.20pm
Price Code D

Trad. arr. Ensemble Bash
Yaa Yaa Kolé   6'

Steve Reich
Music for Pieces of Wood   9'

Cage
Sonatas and Interludes for
Prepared Piano – excerpts   8'

Orphy Robinson
Suite d'Lorenzo   8'

Frederic Rzewski
Winnsboro Cotton Mill Blues   9'

Django Bates
The Catering Trade   15'
London premiere

Trad. arr. Paulinus Bozie
Kumpo   10'

Joanna MacGregor piano
Ensemble Bash

Introducing a theme of this year's Proms, Ensemble Bash (joined by last year's Last Night soloist Joanna MacGregor) presents a dramatic, funny and powerful synthesis that reflects the influences of traditional sounds on the music of our time.

Prom ⑧ PREMIERE NIGHT

Thursday 24 July
7.30pm – c9.50pm
Price Code A

Stravinsky
Petrushka (1947)   32'

I N T E R V A L

Korngold
Violanta (*semi-staged*)   74'
London premiere

Opera North

Simone Trovai
   Jonathan Summers baritone
Violanta **Janice Cairns** soprano
Alfonso **Hans Aschenbach** tenor
Barbara
   Liane Keegan mezzo-soprano
Bice   **Elena Ferrari** soprano
Giovanni Bracca
     Jeffrey Stewart tenor

Nigel Lowery director

Chorus of Opera North
English Northern Philharmonia
Paul Daniel conductor

Erich Wolfgang Korngold, born 100 years ago, was a most gifted prodigy: this gory and erotic tale, written when the composer was only seventeen, is set in Venice against the background of the *commedia dell'arte*, which also lies behind Stravinsky's famous ballet.

Prom 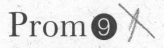 9 ✗

Friday 25 July
7.30pm – c10.00pm
Price Code A

Sir Peter Maxwell Davies
Sails in St Magnus I*   c12'
BBC commission: world premiere

Beethoven
Piano Concerto No. 1
in C major   36'

I N T E R V A L

Shostakovich
Symphony No. 8   60'

Stephen Kovacevich piano

BBC Philharmonic
Vassily Sinaisky conductor
Sir Peter Maxwell Davies
conductor*

Vassily Sinaisky's searing performance of Shostakovich's Eighth Symphony was acclaimed earlier this year in Manchester. The orchestra's Associate Composer Sir Peter Maxwell Davies begins a series of new works inspired by his friend the poet George Mackay Brown, and leading pianist Stephen Kovacevich makes a welcome return to the Proms.

Pre-Prom Talk at 6.15pm: see p139
Sir Peter Maxwell Davies

Prom 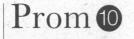 10

Saturday 26 July
7.30pm – c9.40pm
Price Code A

Britten
The Young Person's Guide
to the Orchestra   17'

Grainger
The Warriors   18'

I N T E R V A L

Jonathan Harvey
Percussion Concerto   c25'
BBC commission: world premiere

Elgar
Enigma Variations   30'

Evelyn Glennie percussion

BBC Philharmonic
Richard Hickox conductor

A feast of British music. Two masterpieces, Britten's orchestral display based on Purcell, and Elgar's portraits of his friends, frame two Proms premieres: a new concerto for star percussionist Evelyn Glennie, and Percy Grainger's primal vision of war, drawing on the hypnotic traditions of non-Western music: an astonishing score.

Pre-Prom Talk at 6.15pm: see p139
Jonathan Harvey

Prom 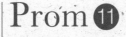 11

Sunday 27 July
7.30pm – c9.45pm
Price Code A

Satie orch. Debussy
Two Gymnopédies   6'

Poulenc
Organ Concerto   21'

I N T E R V A L

Honegger
Joan of Arc at the Stake
(*semi-staged*)   70'

Ian Tracey organ

Fiona Shaw speaker
Eileen Hulse soprano
Sarah Connolly mezzo-soprano
Alice Coote mezzo-soprano
John Graham-Hall tenor

Deborah Warner director

Philharmonic Youth Choir
Royal Liverpool Philharmonic Choir
Royal Liverpool Philharmonic Orchestra
Libor Pešek conductor

Honegger's vivid dramatic tableau comes to the Proms for the first time in a semi-staging by director Deborah Warner with Fiona Shaw as Joan, the visionary saint.

Pre-Prom Talk at 6.15pm: see p139
Deborah Warner (on Joan of Arc)

Prom 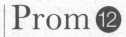 12

Monday 28 July
7.30pm – c9.50pm
Price Code A

Haydn
Symphony No. 31 in D major
'Hornsignal'   26'

Mozart
Clarinet Concerto in A major   28'

I N T E R V A L

Bartók
The Wooden Prince   50'

Paul Meyer clarinet

BBC Symphony Orchestra
David Robertson conductor

Mozart's evergreen Clarinet Concerto, with its serene central movement, links two composers whose music grew out of the central European folk music of their time: *The Wooden Prince*, heard in its rare full version, begins a major Proms retrospective of the music of Béla Bartók. From the same Hungarian roots, Haydn integrates the horn calls of stage-coaches into his marvellously skilful symphony.

Chamber Music at 1.00pm: see p118

Prom ⑬ PREMIERE NIGHT

Tuesday 29 July
7.30pm – c9.40pm
Price Code A

Debussy
The Martyrdom of Saint Sebastian
– Symphonic Fragments   20'

Sofia Gubaidulina
Viola Concerto   c25'
European premiere

I N T E R V A L

Shostakovich
Symphony No. 10 in E minor   50'

Yuri Bashmet viola

Hallé Orchestra
Kent Nagano conductor

Kent Nagano's passionate commitment to the music of our time is well known, as is that of the charismatic violist Yuri Bashmet: they introduce to this country the latest concerto by Sofia Gubaidulina, whose Violin Concerto, *Offertorium*, made such a powerful impact at the Proms. Two landmarks in twentieth-century music complete the programme.

Pre-Prom Talk at 6.15pm: see p139
Sofia Gubaidulina

Prom ⑭

Wednesday 30 July
7.30pm – c9.50pm
Price Code A

Beethoven
Symphony No. 6 in F major
'Pastoral'   43'

I N T E R V A L

Mahler
Das Lied von der Erde   65'

Waltraud Meier mezzo-soprano
Anthony Rolfe Johnson tenor

BBC National Orchestra of Wales
Mark Wigglesworth conductor

Two songs from the earth, reflecting nature in all its glory: Beethoven's loving portrait of the countryside integrates birdsong, peasant dancing and storms into a highly sophisticated symphony, while Mahler's song-cycle explore nature to reveal the deepest issues of life and death. Mark Wigglesworth joins forces with a leading Wagnerian mezzo-soprano, new to the Proms, and an outstanding British tenor.

Prom ⑮ ↗

Thursday 31 July
7.00pm – c9.10pm
Price Code A

David Sawer
the greatest happiness
principle   c15'
BBC commission: London premiere

Bartók
Piano Concerto No. 3   26'

I N T E R V A L

Sibelius
Symphony No. 2 in D major   46'

Stephen Hough piano

BBC National Orchestra of Wales
Mark Wigglesworth conductor

The partnership between Mark Wigglesworth and the BBC National Orchestra of Wales continues to grow, and they have worked together on several BBC commissions, including this new work by a highly-praised British composer. Bartók's concerto is the most lyrical of his three for the piano, and Sibelius's tumultuous Second Symphony is a great Proms favourite.

Pre-Prom Talk at 5.45pm: see p139
David Sawer

Prom ⑯ ↗

Thursday 31 July
10.00pm – c11.15pm
Price Code D

Lassus
Musica Dei donum optimi   4'

Janequin
La Guerre   7'

Sir Peter Maxwell Davies
The House of Winter   10'

Weelkes
Thule, the Period of
Cosmography   5'

Wilbye
Weep, mine eyes   5'

Morley
Fire, fire   3'

György Ligeti
Nonsense Madrigals   14'
London premiere of complete set

Kodály
Evening Song   3'

Lennon & McCartney
Penny Lane, Eleanor Rigby,
I'll follow the Sun, Honey Pie   11'

The King's Singers

The virtuosic King's Singers cross the centuries and expand the Proms repertory to include Beatles songs.

Prom ⑰

Friday 1 August
7.00pm – c9.10pm
Price Code A

Brahms
Song of the Fates .... *12'*

Chopin
Piano Concerto No. 2
in F minor .... *31'*

I N T E R V A L

Schubert
Mass in A flat major .... *46'*

Jean-Yves Thibaudet piano

Rosa Mannion soprano
Stella Doufexis mezzo-soprano
Toby Spence tenor
Nathan Berg bass-baritone

BBC Symphony Chorus
BBC Symphony Orchestra
Jiří Bělohlávek conductor

Three Proms themes come
together: the anniversaries of
both Brahms and Schubert, and
the folk inspiration of Chopin's
concerto, played by a much-loved
Proms soloist. Brahms's vigorous
choral writing contrasts with the
wonderful serenity and repose of
Schubert's symphonic Mass, a
worthy successor to Beethoven.

Prom ⑱

Saturday 2 August
7.30pm – c9.40pm
Price Code B

Gilbert and Sullivan
The Gondoliers

Act 1 .... *55'*

I N T E R V A L

Act 2 .... *40'*

Duke of Plaza-Toro
    Richard Suart baritone
Duchess of Plaza-Toro
    Felicity Palmer mezzo-soprano
Don Alhambra
    Donald Maxwell baritone
Marco **Jamie MacDougall** tenor
Giuseppe
    Jason Howard baritone
Gianetta
    Rosemary Joshua soprano
Tessa **Pamela Helen Stephen**
            mezzo-soprano
Luiz **Timothy Robinson** tenor
Inez **Penelope Walker** contralto

BBC Singers
BBC Concert Orchestra
Barry Wordsworth conductor

The return of Gilbert and
Sullivan to the Proms with a
performance of their most
exuberant and colourful score.

Prom ⑲

Sunday 3 August
4.00pm – c5.30pm
Price Code A

**German Cabaret Songs by
Hanns Eisler, Ilse Weber,
Friedrich Hollaender and
Rudolf Nelson** .... *15'*

Weill
Mahagonny-Songspiel (staged) *25'*
The Seven Deadly Sins (staged) *35'*

Mecklenburgh Opera

Anna **Marie McLaughlin**
soprano
Marianne Rørholm
mezzo-soprano
Jeffrey Lloyd-Roberts tenor
Jonathan Veira baritone
Nicolas Cavallier bass

John Abulafia director

Sinfonia 21
Anne Manson conductor

Kurt Weill is increasingly
recognised as a key voice in
twentieth-century music:
following last year's revival of *The
Silver Lake*, two of his short, bitter
masterpieces are here staged by a
leading young company and
complemented with cabaret songs
of his time.

Prom ⑳ PREMIERE NIGHT

Sunday 3 August
7.30pm – c9.35pm
Price Code A

Glinka
Capriccio brillante on the 'Jota
Aragonesa' .... *9'*

Prokofiev
Violin Concerto No. 2
in G minor .... *28'*

I N T E R V A L

Giya Kancheli
Symphony No. 3 .... *23'*
UK premiere

Tchaikovsky
Francesca da Rimini .... *24'*

Tasmin Little violin

David James counter-tenor

**Royal Scottish National
Orchestra**
Alexander Lazarev conductor

The new Chief Conductor of
the Royal Scottish National
Orchestra shows Glinka using
Spanish folk music, and brings
the haunting sounds of Giya
Kancheli's music to the Proms for
the first time, in a symphony
inspired by the unique singing of
the Rustavi Choir (see Prom 26).

Prom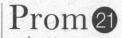

Monday 4 August
7.30pm – c9.40pm
Price Code A

Mahler
Blumine   7'

Roger Reynolds
The Red Act Arias   32'
BBC commission: world premiere

I N T E R V A L

Mahler
Symphony No. 1 in D major   55'

BBC Singers
BBC Symphony Orchestra
Leonard Slatkin conductor

Leonard Slatkin, now Music Director in Washington, DC, returns to the Proms in Mahler's titanic First Symphony, which quotes a version of the well-known melody *Frère Jacques*, with the symphony's extra *Blumine* movement to open the concert. Roger Reynolds's bold new commission combines live sound with recordings of orchestra and singers to surround the audience.

Chamber Music at 1.00pm: see p118
Pre-Prom Talk at 6.15pm: see p139
Roger Reynolds

Prom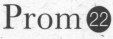

Tuesday 5 August
7.30pm – c9.40pm
Price Code A

Mozart
Symphony No. 35 in D major
'Haffner'   20'

Korngold
Violin Concerto   25'

I N T E R V A L

Markevitch
Rebus   24'
London premiere

Stravinsky
The Firebird – Suite (1919)   21'

Gil Shaham violin

Bournemouth Symphony Orchestra
Yakov Kreizberg conductor

One of Mozart's brightest symphonies and a Stravinsky ballet which owes much to Russian folk music enclose Korngold's Violin Concerto, a lush Romantic score, and a rarity by Igor Markevitch, an individual composer who, as an influential conductor, gave several Stravinsky premieres.

Prom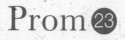

Wednesday 6 August
7.30pm – c9.45pm
Price Code B

Bach
Mass in B minor

Missa (Kyrie, Gloria)   50'

I N T E R V A L

Symbolum Nicenum (Credo),
Sanctus, Benedictus,
Agnus Dei   50'

Susan Chilcott soprano
Catherine Wyn-Rogers mezzo-soprano
John Mark Ainsley tenor
Gerald Finley bass

Choir of The English Concert
The English Concert
Trevor Pinnock conductor

Beethoven's Mass (Prom 1) was written against the background of this great setting by Bach, an object of veneration even in the nineteenth century. Performed as here, with the transparent textures of period instruments and small vocal forces, its colourful scoring and dance-like rhythms complement its old-style fugues and majestic choruses, and reassert its claim to be one of the great universal masterpieces.

Prom 24

Thursday 7 August
7.30pm – c9.40pm
Price Code A

Bartók
Dance Suite   16'

Strauss
Ständchen
Wiegenlied
Ich wollt' ein Sträusslein binden
Säusle, liebe Myrthe
Amor   18'

I N T E R V A L

Mahler
Symphony No. 4 in G major   58'

Inger Dam-Jensen soprano

BBC Scottish Symphony Orchestra
Martyn Brabbins conductor

Mahler drew for inspiration on the music of nature and the countryside, and the idealised vision of his Fourth Symphony captures a world of pastoral innocence. As well as Mahler's vocal finale, the Cardiff Singer of the World winner Inger Dam-Jensen sings Strauss songs, and Bartók's fiery suite of dances pays tribute to the music of his homeland.

Prom 25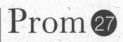

Friday 8 August
7.00pm – c9.10pm
Price Code A

Bartók
Kossuth   18'

Luciano Berio
Folk Songs   21'

I N T E R V A L

Schubert
Rondo in A major   14'

Dvořák
Symphony No. 8 in G major   37'

Michelle DeYoung
mezzo-soprano

BBC Symphony Orchestra
Jiří Bělohlávek conductor

The lilting rhythms and tuneful melodies of Dvořák's ever-popular Eighth Symphony draw inspiration from Czech folk music, but the composer transforms them into a tight-knit symphony. Berio transcribes folk songs literally and clothes them imaginatively. Bartók's early *Kossuth* is far from the violence of his later work: it is a rich and rhapsodic tone-poem which owes much to Strauss.

Prom 26

Friday 8 August
10.00pm – c11.15pm
Price Code D

Georgian Folk Songs   60'

The Rustavi Choir
Ansor Erkomaishvili conductor

Of all the diverse musical traditions of Eastern Europe, the haunting sounds of Georgian choral singing are among the most distinctive and exciting. The all-male Rustavi Choir has a huge repertoire of traditional songs which are by turns simple, sophisticated and downright earthy; their performances and many recordings are famed for their astonishing virtuosity and tonal beauty.

Prom 27

Saturday 9 August
7.30pm – c9.50pm
Price Code A

Sir Michael Tippett
Ritual Dances from 'The Midsummer Marriage'   25'

Vaughan Williams
Symphony No. 6 in E minor   34'

I N T E R V A L

Sibelius
Symphony No. 1 in E minor   39'

National Youth Orchestra of Great Britain
Sir Colin Davis conductor

Well known for his commitment to young people's music-making, Colin Davis last year conducted the European Union Youth Orchestra at the Proms, and here turns to the National Youth Orchestra with three works, all strongly nationalist: Tippett's *Midsummer Marriage* has its roots deep in the British folk consciousness, and Vaughan Williams too was an arranger of folk song; Colin Davis has won the highest praise for his interpretation of Sibelius symphonies.

Prom 28

Sunday 10 August
3.00pm – c5.00pm
Price Code A

Haydn
Sonata No. 52 in E flat major   20'

Liszt
Liebestraum No. 3   4'

Hungarian Rhapsody No. 12 in C sharp minor   10'

I N T E R V A L

Chopin
Two Nocturnes, Op. 27   12'

Piano Sonata No. 3 in B minor, Op. 58   28'

Evgeny Kissin piano

A solo recital is a Proms innovation: of the younger generation of artists few have made as stunning an impression as the Russian phenomenon Evgeny Kissin. His London recitals and recordings have brought the kind of attention reserved for the starriest virtuosi of the past, like Chopin and Liszt themselves. In his Hungarian Rhapsodies, Liszt makes the most of his folk-music roots.

NB The performance will take place in the Arena

Prom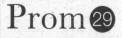

Sunday 10 August
7.30pm – c9.40pm
Price Code C

Schubert
Stabat Mater in G minor 7'

Gesang der Geister über den
Wassern, D714 10'

Psalm 23 6'

Hymnus an den heiligen Geist 7'

I N T E R V A L

Beethoven
Symphony No. 9 in D minor
'Choral' 61'

Luba Orgonasova soprano
Bernarda Fink mezzo-soprano
Gordon Gietz tenor
Bryn Terfel bass-baritone

Monteverdi Choir
**Orchestre Révolutionnaire et
Romantique**
John Eliot Gardiner conductor

Beethoven's Ninth, a long-standing Proms tradition, was given a memorable large-scale reading last year; this is a contrasting approach, by a leading conductor using period instruments. It is prefaced by some of the most beautiful smaller-scale choral music of Schubert.

Prom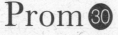

Monday 11 August
7.30pm – c9.45pm
Price Code A

Magnus Lindberg
New work 15'
world premiere

Sibelius
Violin Concerto in D minor 32'

I N T E R V A L

Beethoven
Symphony No. 3 in E flat major
'Eroica' 50'

Christian Tetzlaff violin

**Finnish Radio Symphony
Orchestra**
Jukka-Pekka Saraste conductor

Beethoven's mighty 'Eroica' Symphony ends with a finale that creates its magnificent effect from a popular *contredanse*. The young violinist Christian Tetzlaff returns to the Proms with a classic of the repertory, and the concert opens with a new work by one of the most sought-after composers of the day, who directed the South Bank Centre's 'Meltdown' festival last year.

Chamber Music at 1.00pm: see p118
Pre-Prom Talk at 6.15pm: see p139
Magnus Lindberg

Prom

Tuesday 12 August
7.00pm – c9.05pm
Price Code A

Ravel
Le Tombeau de Couperin 17'

Bartók
Four Pieces for Orchestra,
Op. 12 24'

Pierre Boulez
Notations I–IV 11'

I N T E R V A L

Stravinsky
The Rite of Spring 34'

Gustav Mahler Youth Orchestra
Pierre Boulez conductor

Pierre Boulez is a central figure in the music of our time, whose *Rite of Spring* in London earlier this year was acclaimed as 'stupendous'. He returns to the Proms in a programme of twentieth-century classics. *Notations* are dazzling reworkings of four of Boulez's early piano pieces, mirrored by Bartók's rarely-heard Four Pieces, and joined by masterpieces by Stravinsky and Ravel.

Pre-Prom Talk at 5.45pm: see p139
Pierre Boulez

Prom

Tuesday 12 August
10.00pm – c11.25pm
Price Code D

Lou Harrison
New First Suite for Strings 16'
UK premiere

Stephen Montague
Concerto for piano and orchestra c25'
BBC commission: world premiere

Barber
Adagio for Strings 8'

Colin McPhee
Tabuh-tabuhan: Toccata for two
pianos and orchestra* 20'

Rolf Hind piano
Thomas Adès piano*

**Orchestra of St John's, Smith
Square**
John Lubbock conductor

Samuel Barber's moving *Adagio* has been topping the charts this year. A new concerto by American-born Stephen Montague, and a work by the eighty-year-old pioneer Lou Harrison, join the brilliant gamelan-inspired piece by the Canadian composer Colin McPhee, who was a major influence on Britten.

Prom ㉝

Wednesday 13 August
7.30pm – *c*10.00pm
Price Code A

George Benjamin
Ringed by the Flat Horizon ⟩ 19'

Bartók
Violin Concerto No. 2   38'

I N T E R V A L

Berlioz
Symphonie fantastique   55'

Viktoria Mullova violin

BBC Symphony Orchestra
Andrew Davis conductor

Under Andrew Davis, Chief Conductor since 1989, the BBC Symphony Orchestra is about to make a two-concert visit to the Salzburg Festival, taking this classic piece by the British composer George Benjamin that was heard at the Proms in 1980. Orchestra and conductor have made a speciality of Berlioz, and their contribution to the Bartók theme brings a leading international violinist back to the Proms.

Pre-Prom Talk at 6.15pm: see p139
George Benjamin

Prom ㉞

Thursday 14 August
7.30pm – *c*9.40pm
Price Code B

Tchaikovsky
Romeo and Juliet   20'

Shostakovich
From Jewish Folk Poetry   28'

I N T E R V A L

Rimsky-Korsakov
Sheherazade   42'

Marina Shaguch soprano
Larissa Diadkova
mezzo-soprano
Evgeny Akimov tenor

Kirov Orchestra
Valery Gergiev conductor

The charismatic conductor Valery Gergiev returns after his Proms debut last season, this time with his own orchestra from the Maryinsky Theatre, St Petersburg, in a programme that introduces Shostakovich's intense settings of folk poetry to the Proms for the first time, in between two scintillating and colourful classics of the Russian repertory.

Prom ㉟ ⤴

Friday 15 August
7.00pm – *c*9.10pm
Price Code A

Bartók
Romanian Folk Dances (solo piano and orchestral versions)   12'

Hungarian Sketches (solo piano and orchestral versions)   8'

Piano Concerto No. 1   24'

I N T E R V A L

Brahms
Hungarian Dances Nos. 1 & 10   5'

Symphony No. 2 in D major   42'

András Schiff piano

Budapest Festival Orchestra
Iván Fischer conductor

András Schiff is a unique musician, an ever-adventurous explorer of the repertory, and at the heart of this year's Bartók survey is this fascinating juxtaposition of his use, in both piano and orchestral music, of Hungarian folk song. Brahms too uses Hungarian music in his orchestral dances, and his towering Second Symphony completes a fascinating programme.

Prom ㊱ ⤴

Friday 15 August
10.00pm – *c*11.20pm
Price Code D

Purcell
My Heart is Inditing   16'

Fayrfax
Magnificat regale   14'

Byrd
Domine quis habitat   9'

Sheppard
Verbum caro factum est   7'

Handel
Let God Arise   21'

BBC Singers
Brandenburg Consort
Stephen Cleobury conductor

The great tradition of British choral music is explored at the start of a special weekend which coincides with a conference – at the Royal College of Music – of the world's leading musical scholars (see also Proms Chamber Music, page 118): the intricately expressive music of the English Renaissance is framed by the ceremonial splendour of a coronation anthem by Purcell and a Chandos anthem by Handel.

Prom  37

Saturday 16 August
7.00pm – c9.15pm
Price Code A

Schubert
Symphony No. 5 in B flat major 27'

Britten
Serenade for Tenor, Horn and
Strings 23'

I N T E R V A L

Wagner
Siegfried Idyll 19'

Mendelssohn
Symphony No. 4 in A 'Italian' 27'

Ian Bostridge tenor
Timothy Brown horn

Norwegian Chamber Orchestra
Iona Brown conductor

A welcome return to the Proms by one of the finest European chamber orchestras. A two-day celebration of Britten's vocal music begins with one of his very finest works, performed by one of the great rising stars among British singers, and this lyrical programme also includes popular symphonies by two featured Proms composers.

Prom  38

Britten Weekend
Saturday 16 August
10.00pm – c11.15pm
Price Code D

Britten
The Prodigal Son (staged) 66'

City of Birmingham Touring Opera

Tempter   **Ivan Sharpe** tenor
Father
    Charles Johnston baritone
Elder Son
    Quentin Hayes baritone
Younger Son
    Andrew Burden tenor

Mark Tinkler director
Simon Halsey musical director
Birmingham Contemporary Music Group

B ritten's strikingly simple retelling of this well-known Biblical story was the last of his three Church Parables, which all have their roots deep in both Western and Eastern folk traditions. Mark Tinkler's ingenious production – which sets the story in the 1930s – features an exceptional young cast and was a highly-praised part of this year's Towards the Millennium series in Birmingham and London.

Prom  39

Britten Weekend
Sunday 17 August
4.00pm – c5.20pm
Price Code D

Britten
A Ceremony of Carols 22'
Six Metamorphoses after Ovid 13'
Hymn to St Peter 6'
A Hymn to the Virgin 5'
Rejoice in the Lamb 17'

Aline Brewer harp
Nicholas Daniel oboe
Martin Baker organ

Westminster Abbey Choir
Martin Neary conductor

C horal music, and the sound of the human voice, were at the heart of Britten's output, and this sequence by the world-famous Westminster Abbey Choir draws together some of his finest pieces in the genre. It is punctuated by a vivid piece for solo oboe played by the soloist whose premiere of John Woolrich's Oboe Concerto was a highlight of last season.

BBC Proms Lecture by Philip Brett at 6.00pm: see page 139

Prom  40

Britten Weekend
Sunday 17 August
8.00pm – c9.35pm
Price Code B

Britten
War Requiem 85'

Eva Urbanová soprano
Hans Peter Blochwitz tenor
Thomas Hampson baritone

Choristers of Westminster Abbey
City of Birmingham Symphony Chorus
BBC Symphony Chorus
BBC Symphony Orchestra
Andrew Davis conductor

'M y subject is war, and the pity of war': Wilfrid Owen's words haunt this powerful and now classic work, written for Coventry Cathedral in 1962, which juxtaposes Owen's poetry with the traditional texts of the Requiem Mass to moving effect. The inspiration of older models (such as Verdi's *Requiem* in Prom 72) is present, but Britten's synthesis of individual human drama and timeless choral ritual is wholly original. This international cast will take the work to the Salzburg Festival for the first time this week.

Prom 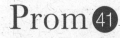41

Monday 18 August
7.30pm – c9.35pm
Price Code A

Glinka
Kamarinskaya   7'

Tchaikovsky
Piano Concerto No. 1
in B flat minor   33'

I N T E R V A L

Edward McGuire
Calgacus   17'
London premiere

Shostakovich
Symphony No. 1 in F minor   30'

Grigory Sokolov piano

Robert Wallace highland bagpipe

**BBC Scottish Symphony
Orchestra**
Osmo Vänskä conductor

The drone of bagpipes and the folk songs of Russia are joined by Shostakovich's precocious First Symphony and one of the most popular concertos in the repertory in this stimulating mixture.

Chamber Music at 1.00pm: see p118
Pre-Prom Talk at 6.30pm: see p139
Edward McGuire

Prom 42 ⤴

Tuesday 19 August
7.00pm – c9.00pm
Price Code A

Beethoven
Overture 'Namensfeier'   7'

Mendelssohn
Die erste Walpurgisnacht   32'

I N T E R V A L

Berlioz
Harold in Italy   42'

Thomas Zehetmair viola

Patricia Bardon mezzo-soprano
Paul Charles Clarke tenor
Thomas Hampson baritone
Neal Davies bass

**Choir of the Enlightenment
Orchestra of the Age of
Enlightenment**
Mark Elder conductor

The spirit of Brahms hovers over this fascinating programme: he conducted all three works in Vienna in 1873–4. Mendelssohn's colourful Goethe setting (see page 20) comes to the Proms for the first time, and the tangy sonorities of period instruments will enhance Berlioz's mellow, viola-dominated textures.

Prom 43 ⤴

Tuesday 19 August
10.00pm – c11.30pm
Price Code D

Oliver Knussen
Two Organa   6'

Simon Bainbridge
Landscape and Memory   15'

Sir Harrison Birtwistle
Ritual Fragment   11'

George Benjamin
Three Inventions   17'

Thomas Adès
Living Toys   17'

Michael Thompson horn

London Sinfonietta
Markus Stenz conductor

The tremendous vitality and originality of the British new music scene will be dazzlingly demonstrated by these pieces of the 1990s that have already become classics, performed by the crack ensemble that has done so much to nurture and support composers in this country under its charismatic Principal Conductor.

Prom 44

Wednesday 20 August
7.30pm – c9.50pm
Price Code A

Sibelius
The Wood Nymph   21'
London premiere

Luonnotar   9'

I N T E R V A L

Sibelius
Kullervo Symphony   72'

Kirsi Tiihonen soprano
Jukka Rasilainen baritone

**Helsinki University Male Chorus
BBC Scottish Symphony
Orchestra**
Osmo Vänskä conductor

An outstanding symphony cycle in Scotland earlier this year brought Osmo Vänskä to the forefront of attention as a Sibelius interpreter. Now he adds to his highly-praised collaboration with the BBC Scottish the great choral epic *Kullervo*, as well as bringing to London the newly rediscovered tone-poem *The Wood Nymph*, both inspired by Finnish story-telling traditions.

Pre-Prom Talk at 6.15pm: see p139
Osmo Vänskä (on Sibelius)

Prom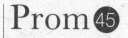

Thursday 21 August
7.30pm – c9.35pm
Price Code A

Schubert
Symphony No. 3 in D major   24'

Schubert orch. Brahms
An Schwager Kronos
Geheimes
Gruppe aus dem Tartarus
Memnon   12'

Schubert orch. Berlioz
Erlkönig   4'

I N T E R V A L

Brahms
Symphony No. 4 in E minor   40'

Thomas Allen baritone

London Philharmonic Orchestra
Sir Charles Mackerras
conductor

To celebrate the anniversaries
of both Schubert and
Brahms, a programme of great
symphonies (Brahms edited
Schubert's symphonies for
publication) enclosing the
transcriptions that Brahms made
of Lieder by Schubert, an act of
homage from one master
songwriter to another.

Prom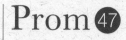

Friday 22 August
7.30pm – c9.30pm
Price Code A

Schubert
Symphony No. 8 in B minor
'Unfinished'   24'

Beethoven
Ah! Perfido   13'

I N T E R V A L

Mozart
Ch'io mi scordi di te   10'

Hindemith
Symphony 'Mathis der Maler'   28'

Amanda Roocroft soprano

Malcolm Martineau piano

Royal Philharmonic Orchestra
Daniele Gatti conductor

The Royal Philharmonic's
dynamic Principal Conductor
brings together Viennese music –
powerful vocal set-pieces by
Mozart and Beethoven, and
Schubert's tenderest symphony –
and contrasts it with the
imaginative power of
Hindemith's portrait of the
painter Mathias Grünewald.

Prom 47

Saturday 23 August
7.30pm – c9.35pm
Price Code A

Sibelius
En Saga   15'

Grieg
Piano Concerto in A minor   30'

I N T E R V A L

Rodion Shchedrin
Old Russian Circus Music   24'
UK premiere

Tchaikovsky
Capriccio italien   16'

Ilya Itin piano

BBC Philharmonic
Vassily Sinaisky conductor

Tchaikovsky's rousing *Capriccio
italien* shows how popular
music permeated his work, while
a living Russian composer makes
use of his own folk heritage in an
amusing homage, and the highly-
praised recent winner of the
Leeds Piano Competition plays
one of the most popular of all
piano concertos.

Prom 48

Sunday 24 August
3.00pm – c5.00pm
Price Code A

Bartók
Divertimento   25'

Haydn
Cello Concerto No. 1
in C major   25'

I N T E R V A L

Schubert
Symphony No. 4 in C minor
'Tragic'   30'

Natalie Clein cello

**National Youth Chamber
Orchestra**
Roger Norrington conductor

Leading conductor Roger
Norrington brings a chamber
orchestra of senior members of
the National Youth Orchestra to
the Proms, with a winner of the
BBC Young Musician of the Year,
cellist Natalie Clein. Her Haydn
concerto is aptly heard alongside
Bartók's striking homage to the
world of the eighteenth century
and a darkly powerful but always
lyrical Schubert symphony.

*NB Half price for under 14s
(not restricted view, Arena or Gallery)*

Prom 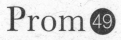49

Sunday 24 August
7.30pm – *c*9.40pm
Price Code A

Roy Harris
Symphony No. 3   17'

Barber
Violin Concerto   24'

INTERVAL

Tchaikovsky
Symphony No. 5 in E minor   48'

Joshua Bell violin

Dallas Symphony Orchestra
Andrew Litton conductor

Tchaikovsky's dramatic and deeply Romantic Fifth Symphony is played on the first European tour by the Dallas Symphony with their new Music Director Andrew Litton, who was a popular Proms visitor when he conducted the Bournemouth Symphony. They bring two outstanding works from their country, perhaps the finest American symphony and concerto of the century, with one of the world's leading violinists.

Prom 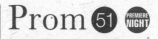50

Monday 25 August
7.00pm – *c*9.45pm
Price Code B

Rossini
Count Ory (*semi-staged*)

Act 1   65'

INTERVAL

Act 2   65'

Glyndebourne Festival Opera

Count Ory **Tracey Welborn** tenor
Raimbaud
             Ludovic Tezier baritone
Countess Adele
             Annick Massis soprano
The Tutor
             Julien Robbins baritone
Isolier
Diana Montague mezzo-soprano
Dame Ragonde
             Jane Shaulis mezzo-soprano

The Glyndebourne Chorus
London Philharmonic Orchestra
Andrew Davis conductor

A deliciously entertaining comic opera which is sure to be a highlight of the season. Richard Osborne writes about Rossini's wit on page 54.

Chamber Music at 1.00pm: see p118

Prom 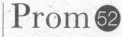51

Tuesday 26 August
7.30pm – *c*9.45pm
Price Code A

Elliott Carter
Holiday Overture   9'

Britten
Suite on English Folk Tunes
'A Time There Was ...'   14'

Mark-Anthony Turnage
Dispelling the Fears   20'
London premiere

INTERVAL

Elliott Carter
Allegro scorrevole   12'
European premiere

Ruth Crawford Seeger
Andante   4'

Folk-song settings for orchestra
by Ruth Crawford Seeger,
Charles Seeger and Copland   9'

Copland
Billy the Kid – Suite   20'

Håkan Hardenberger trumpet
John Wallace trumpet

BBC Symphony Orchestra
Oliver Knussen conductor

A stimulating Knussen mix: folk songs (English and American), cowboy songs, and a major Carter premiere.

Pre-Prom Talk at 6.15pm: see p139
Elliott Carter

Prom 52

Wednesday 27 August
7.30pm – *c*9.40pm
Price Code B

Hans Werner Henze
Second Sonata for Strings   15'
UK premiere

Mendelssohn
Violin Concerto in E minor   26'

INTERVAL

Schubert
Symphony No. 9
'Great C major'   55'

Leila Josefowicz violin

Leipzig Gewandhaus Orchestra
Sir Neville Marriner conductor

The first of two programmes by one of Europe's most distinguished musical institutions, each consisting of great works which the orchestra premiered. Mendelssohn directed Schubert's grandest symphony in 1839, while Henze's athletic tribute to the Gewandhaus strings was premiered last year. A rising virtuoso plays the brilliant concerto Mendelssohn wrote for the orchestra's leader, Ferdinand David, in her Proms debut.

Prom 53

Thursday 28 August
7.00pm – c9.00pm
Price Code C

Wagner
Overture 'The Mastersingers
of Nuremberg'   10'

Schumann
Piano Concerto in A minor   30'

I N T E R V A L

Mendelssohn
Symphony No. 3 in A minor
'Scottish'   38'

Alfred Brendel piano

Leipzig Gewandhaus Orchestra
Sir Neville Marriner conductor

One of the greatest living pianists, who collaborates regularly with Sir Neville Marriner, plays the concerto Schumann wrote for his wife, Clara. Mendelssohn's symphony is full of the sounds of a country which inspired so many Romantic poets and composers, and Wagner's overture is one of his grandest and most popular orchestral pieces.

Prom 54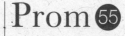

Thursday 28 August
10.00pm – c11.15pm
Price Code D

Schütz
Saul, Saul
Selig sind die Toten
Wie lieblich sind deine
Wohnungen   15'

Scheidt
Zion spricht   7'

Bach
Motet 'Fürchte dich nicht'   8'

Mendelssohn
Three sacred pieces   8'

Brahms
Warum ist das Licht gegeben?   10'

Schoenberg
Friede auf Erden   8'

BBC Singers
Bo Holten conductor

Brahms was fascinated by earlier music; he edited and conducted many German works, including several of tonight's pieces, which form a background to one of his own finest choral compositions.

Prom 55

Friday 29 August
7.30pm – c9.40pm
Price Code A

Programme to include:

Gershwin
Overture 'Strike Up The Band'   6'

John Dankworth
Shakespeare Songs   10'

**Songs by Anne Ronnell and
Billie Holiday**   9'

John Dankworth
Suite 'What the Dickens' –
excerpts   9'

Duke Ellington
Caravan   4'

I N T E R V A L

John Dankworth
New work (for BBC Big Band)   5'
world premiere

Zodiac Variations – excerpts   12'

**Songs by Gershwin and
Ellington**   30'

Cleo Laine singer

The Dankworth Sextet
BBC Big Band
BBC Concert Orchestra
John Dankworth conductor

A joint seventieth-birthday tribute to two of the greatest entertainers on the British jazz scene.

Prom 56

Saturday 30 August
7.30pm – c9.25pm
Price Code A

Dvořák
Overture 'Carnival'   9'

Lutoslawski
Cello Concerto   23'

I N T E R V A L

Brahms
Symphony No. 1 in C minor   46'

Paul Watkins cello

BBC Symphony Orchestra
Tadaaki Otaka conductor

'Beethoven's Tenth' is how contemporaries saw Brahms's First, a new symphony written by a composer with an acute awareness of history. Lutoslawski's witty, pungent concerto is played by the fine principal cellist of the BBC Symphony Orchestra.

Prom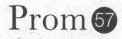

Sunday 31 August
7.30pm – c9.25pm
Price Code A

Sibelius
Symphony No. 3 in C major   *30'*

I N T E R V A L

Britten
Les Illuminations   *23'*

Stravinsky
Symphony in Three Movements *22'*

Dawn Upshaw soprano

Swedish Radio Symphony Orchestra
Esa-Pekka Salonen conductor

A leading conductor of the modern repertory returns to the Proms with the Swedish orchestra he has directed for many years, in two classic reworkings of symphonic form from our century. Following her huge success last year in a solo Prom concert, Dawn Upshaw contributes to our Britten survey with his wonderful Rimbaud settings.

Prom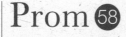

Monday 1 September
7.00pm – c10.05pm
Price Code A

Handel
Jephtha

Act 1   *60'*

I N T E R V A L

Acts 2 and 3   *95'*

Iphis	**Joan Rodgers** soprano	
Storge		
	Felicity Palmer mezzo-soprano	
Hamor		
	Michael Chance counter-tenor	
Jephtha		
	Anthony Rolfe Johnson tenor	
Zebul	**Alastair Miles** bass	
Angel	**Deborah York** soprano	

The New Company
Scottish Chamber Orchestra
Sir Charles Mackerras
conductor

H andel's sublime and moving last oratorio, whose composition was interrupted by his blindness, receives a first Proms performance, with outstanding British singers under a great Handel champion, Sir Charles Mackerras.

Chamber Music at 1.00pm: see p118

Prom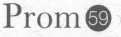

Tuesday 2 September
7.30pm – c9.20pm
Price Code B

Strauss
Prelude to Act 1 of 'Guntram'   *10'*
Death and Transfiguration   *22'*

I N T E R V A L

Strauss
Don Quixote   *42'*

Ken Hakii viola
Godfried Hoogeveen cello

Royal Concertgebouw Orchestra
Riccardo Chailly conductor

T he glorious sound of Amsterdam's Royal Concertgebouw Orchestra – regular and favourite visitors to the Proms – will be heard to full effect in this richly-scored all-Strauss programme under their Music Director, a renowned conductor of the late Romantic repertory.

Prom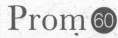

Wednesday 3 September
7.30pm – c9.35pm
Price Code B

Keuris
Three Preludes   *7'*
UK premiere

Rakhmaninov
Piano Concerto No. 2
in C minor   *35'*

I N T E R V A L

Bartók
The Miraculous Mandarin   *31'*

Strauss
Dance of the Seven Veils
from 'Salome'   *10'*

Arkady Volodos piano

Royal Concertgebouw Orchestra
Riccardo Chailly conductor

A brilliant young Russian soloist who has shot to fame in the last couple of seasons plays one of the most popular of all piano concertos, and the Concertgebouw contribute one of Bartók's fiercest scores to our survey of his music; they add a tribute to a leading Dutch composer, Tristan Keuris, who died last year.

Prom 61 ↗

Thursday 4 September
7.00pm – c9.00pm
Price Code: A

Mozart
Piano Concerto No. 25
in C major, K503   *30'*

I N T E R V A L

Ravel
Daphnis and Chloë   *55'*

Alfredo Perl piano

BBC Singers
Royal Liverpool Philharmonic Choir
BBC Philharmonic
Yan Pascal Tortelier conductor

Yan Pascal Tortelier, a conductor with great authority in French music, here brings to the Proms the finest of all French ballet scores in its full version with chorus. Ravel's sensuous, evocative music finds a foil in a performance of Mozart's grandest piano concerto, played by a young pianist who gave a successful Beethoven sonata cycle in London this year.

Prom 62 ↗

Thursday 4 September
10.00pm – c11.25pm
Price Code D

Brahms
Clarinet Quintet in B minor   *38'*

Mendelssohn
Octet in E flat major   *36'*

Hausmusik London

The gypsy-inspired swirlings of the slow movement of Brahms's Clarinet Quintet are a wonderful instance of a composer transforming folk music into classical form. The autumnal glow of this great chamber work will be ideally suited to the period instruments of this outstanding ensemble, and will contrast with the bubbling high spirits and infectious enthusiasm of Mendelssohn's teenage Octet for strings.

NB The performance will take place in the Arena

Prom 63

Friday 5 September
7.30pm – c9.45pm
Price Code A

Monteverdi
Madrigals from Book 8   *30'*

Gabrieli Consort and Players
Paul McCreesh director

I N T E R V A L

Hans Werner Henze
Venus and Adonis   *75'*
UK premiere

Evelyn Herlitzius soprano
Ekkehard Wlaschiha baritone

BBC Symphony Orchestra
Markus Stenz conductor

Henze's sumptuous score, one of the most successful new operas of our time, was widely praised at its Munich premiere earlier this year as 'a great big Romantic score'. Its Italian warmth is aptly preceded by dramatic madrigals of love and war by Monteverdi, whose music has been a source of inspiration for Henze.

Prom 64

Saturday 6 September
7.30pm – c9.40pm
Price Code A

Poulenc
Gloria   *24'*

Ravel
Piano Concerto in G major   *23'*

I N T E R V A L

Rakhmaninov
Symphony No. 1 in D minor   *44'*

Judith Howarth soprano

Louis Lortie piano

City of Birmingham Symphony Chorus
BBC National Chorus of Wales
BBC National Orchestra of Wales
David Atherton conductor

Rakhmaninov's dramatic First Symphony was premiered a hundred years ago, and its late-Romantic splendour is complemented by Ravel's jazz-tinged concerto, played by the pianist who was such a hit here last year, with Poulenc's joyful *Gloria* providing a suitably rousing opening.

Prom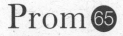

Sunday 7 September
7.30pm – c9.45pm
Price Code A

Brahms
Rinaldo   42'

I N T E R V A L

Prokofiev
Violin Concerto No. 1
in D major   22'

Sibelius
Symphony No. 5 in E flat major 30'

Stig Andersen tenor

Chantal Juillet violin

Orphei Drängar
Gothenburg Symphony
Orchestra
Neeme Järvi conductor

Neeme Järvi, famous as a champion of unjustly neglected repertoire, here treats Proms audiences to a rare performance of Brahms's heroic cantata for tenor, male voices and orchestra based on Goethe's tale of a knight who has to decide between love and duty. A popular concerto and a much-loved symphony of this century show off Järvi's orchestra at its peak.

Prom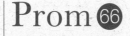

Monday 8 September
2.30pm – c4.15pm

Junior Prom
'Wet Wet Wet!'

Tony Robinson presenter

New London Children's Choir
BBC Concert Orchestra
Ronald Corp conductor

Water rules our lives: we need it, we drink it, we wash in it, we swim in it, we sail on it, and get rained on by it. Following the huge success of last year's first-ever Junior Prom for 6- to 14-year-olds, Tony Robinson explores the wonderful world of water in music across the ages.

Special booking arrangements apply.
For further information please call
0171 765 5666

Chamber Music at 1.00pm: see p118

Prom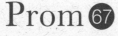

Monday 8 September
7.30pm – c9.40pm
Price Code A

Stravinsky
Oedipus Rex   52'

I N T E R V A L

Bartók
Concerto for Orchestra   38'

Oedipus **Anthony Rolfe Johnson**
tenor
Jocasta   **Anne Sofie von Otter**
mezzo-soprano
Creon/Messenger
Alan Opie baritone
Shepherd
Jon Runar Arason tenor
Tiresias **Ronnie Johansen** bass

Orphei Drängar
Gothenburg Symphony
Orchestra
Neeme Järvi conductor

Two massive masterpieces of our century – Bartók's late, popular showpiece and Stravinsky's neo-Classical sound-sculpture – make a uniquely powerful combination.

Prom 68

Tuesday 9 September
7.30pm – c9.45pm
Price Code B

Beethoven
Piano Concerto No. 4
in G major   33'

I N T E R V A L

Bruckner
Symphony No. 7 in E major   66'

Emanuel Ax piano
European Union Youth
Orchestra
Bernard Haitink conductor

The lyrical strength and architectural pacing of Bernard Haitink's Bruckner performances are outstanding, and here he works with the superb young musicians of the European Union Youth Orchestra in one of the greatest symphonies. The leading Polish-American pianist Emanuel Ax returns to the Proms in Beethoven's Fourth Concerto, whose breathtakingly original opening ushers in a new world for the concerto.

Prom  69

Wednesday 10 September
7.00pm – c9.10pm
Price Code A

Mendelssohn
Symphony No. 5 in D major
'Reformation'   27'

I N T E R V A L

Brahms
A German Requiem   70'

Solveig Kringelborn soprano
Peter Mattei baritone

Philharmonia Chorus
BBC Symphony Chorus
BBC Symphony Orchestra
Claus Peter Flor conductor

Brahms's inspired setting of German texts on death and Mendelssohn's fervent symphony both draw on great traditional German chorales. Claus Peter Flor returns to the Proms with leading soloists and a huge chorus in an ideal Albert Hall programme.

Prom 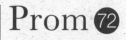 70

Wednesday 10 September
10.00pm – c11.10pm
Price Code D

Mozart
Fantasia in F minor, K608   11'

Thomas Trotter organ

Mozart
Serenade in B flat major for
13 Wind Instruments, K361
'Gran Partita'   45'

**City of Birmingham Symphony
Orchestra Wind Ensemble**
Sir Simon Rattle conductor

Simon Rattle and his Birmingham musicians give their first late-evening Prom with a perfect night-time work: Mozart's Serenade for thirteen wind instruments, effortlessly lyrical and inventive in its use of wind sonorities. Its achingly beautiful Adagio was one of the Mozart works used to great effect in the play and film *Amadeus*. To start, a magnificently fugal Fantasia for organ that re-creates the Baroque in Mozart's image.

Prom 71

Thursday 11 September
7.30pm – c9.55pm
Price Code C

Shostakovich
Violin Concerto No.1
in A minor   36'

I N T E R V A L

Mahler
Symphony No. 5   75'

Maxim Vengerov violin

**City of Birmingham Symphony
Orchestra**
Sir Simon Rattle conductor

One of the leading violinists to have emerged in recent years plays the intense and powerful concerto with which he made his reputation. Simon Rattle, who has made such a strong feature of Mahler with his Birmingham orchestra, conducts one of the most popular symphonies for the first time in London.

Prom 72

Friday 12 September
7.30pm – c9.05pm
Price Code C

Verdi
Requiem   85'

Michèle Crider soprano
Olga Borodina mezzo-soprano
Frank Lopardo tenor
René Pape bass

London Voices
London Symphony Chorus
London Symphony Orchestra
Sir Georg Solti conductor

Sir Georg Solti returned to the Proms last year with a triumphant Beethoven Ninth; now another classic of the choral repertory, Verdi's *Requiem*, provides a culmination of this season's settings of the Mass with its operatically extrovert and extraordinarily vivid response to the timeless words of the Requiem.

Prom ⑦³ The Last Night of the Proms

Saturday 13 September
7.30pm – c10.30pm
Price Code E

Handel
Zadok the Priest   5'

Brahms
Variations on the St Anthony
Chorale   17'

Judith Weir
Sanctus   7'
UK premiere

Messiaen
'Transports de Joie' from
'L'Ascension'   4'

Wagner
Prelude and Liebestod from
'Tristan and Isolde'   17'

I N T E R V A L

John Adams
Short Ride in a Fast Machine   4'

Gershwin
Variations on 'I Got Rhythm'   9'

Britten
Irish Reel   c4'
London premiere

Weber
'Leise, leise' from
'Der Freischütz'   8'

Elgar
Pomp and Circumstance March
No. 1 in D major   5'

arr. Henry Wood
Fantasia on British Sea-Songs   12'

Arne
Rule, Britannia!   5'

Parry orch. Elgar
Jerusalem   2'

Wayne Marshall organ & piano

Anne Evans soprano

BBC Singers
BBC Symphony Chorus
BBC Symphony Orchestra
Andrew Davis conductor

Drawing together the season's anniversaries and themes, Brahms's loving variations on a traditional tune, John Adams's perky fanfare, and Britten's hilarious *Irish Reel* set in context two substantial vocal contributions by our leading Wagnerian soprano Anne Evans. A small choral classic by Scots composer Judith Weir, the exuberance of Wayne Marshall on both organ and piano, plus the traditional junketings of the Last Night make a heady musical brew: if you can't be there, join the crowds in Hyde Park (see page 136).

Proms Chamber Music

Proms Chamber Music at the V&A

This year the BBC and the Victoria & Albert Museum have combined forces to present Proms Chamber Music in the magnificent Lecture Theatre at the V&A, just a few minutes walk from the Royal Albert Hall.

For further information please see Edward Blakeman's article on page 86.

For booking details please see opposite page.

Concert 1

Monday 21 July
1.00pm – c2.00pm

Webern
Slow Movement

Schubert
String Quintet

Endellion Quartet
Robert Cohen cello

Concert 5

Monday 18 August
1.00pm – c2.00pm

'Alleluias' from the Winchester Troper and Fountains Abbey Manuscript, and by Christopher Fox

Ockeghem
Ut heremita solus

Josquin Desprez
Nymphes des bois

'In Nomines' by Tye, Gibbons, and Ivan Moody

Christopher Fox
A Glimpse of Sion's Glory
London premiere

Fretwork
Orlando Consort

Concert 2

Monday 28 July
1.00pm – c2.00pm

Brahms
Ballade in B major, Op. 10 No. 4

Stephen Montague
Southern Lament
London premiere

Brahms
Variations and Fugue on a Theme by Handel

Stephen Kovacevich piano

Concert 6

Monday 25 August
1.00pm – c2.00pm

'Sins of My Old Age' – a Rossini Soirée re-creating one of his famous Saturday Evening Concerts in Paris in the 1850s. With music by Rossini, Mozart, Chopin, Liszt and others ...

Iain Burnside piano
Artur Pizarro piano
Katarina Karnéus mezzo-soprano
William Dazeley baritone

Concert **3**

Monday 4 August
1.00pm – c2.00pm

Plainsong Magnificat
(Tonus Peregrinus)

Arvo Pärt
Seven Magnificat Antiphons

interspersed with
Grainger
Folk Song Settings including:
Song of Vermeland; My love's in
Germanie; Brigg Fair; Shenandoah;
O Mistress Mine

Polyphony
Stephen Layton conductor

Concert **4**

Monday 11 August
1.00pm – c2.00pm

Britten
String Quartet No. 3

Bartók
String Quartet No. 5

Henschel Quartet

Concert **7**

Monday 1 September
1.00pm – c2.00pm

Jolivet
Suite for Flute, Viola and Harp
Incantation No. 2 for solo flute

Bax
Elegiac Trio

Debussy
Syrinx for solo flute
Sonata for Flute, Viola and Harp

Emily Beynon flute
Michael Gieler viola
Catherine Beynon harp

Concert **8**

Monday 8 September
1.00pm – c2.00pm

A selection of Lieder by
Schubert and French folk song
arrangements by Britten

Joan Rodgers soprano
Roger Vignoles piano

Booking Details

Tickets for each concert, priced
£5.00, can be reserved in
advance via the Royal Albert Hall
Ticket Shop by using the
booking form on page 131 or by
ringing or visiting the Ticket
Shop (0171 589 8212) after 16
June.

On the day of the concert,
tickets can only be bought at the
V&A and will be available at the
Museum ticket desks, priced
£6.50.

In both cases your ticket will also
give you access, after the
concert, to the Museum itself.

A limited number of seats will be
set aside for BBC Proms season
ticket holders, who can obtain a
ticket for free if reserved (by
phone or in person) and
collected before the day of the
concert from the Royal Albert
Hall Ticket Shop. Season ticket
holders will be required to
present both their concert ticket
and their season ticket to secure
admission on the day.

Proms Chamber Music

How to Prom

What is Promming?

Over 1,000 tickets are available at each Proms concert for those members of the audience who are happy to stand to listen to the performance.

There are two standing areas – the **Arena**, which is located directly in front of the stage, and the **Gallery**, located at the top of the Hall.

For further information please see Edward Bhesania's article on page 90.

Tickets available on the night

A high proportion of Arena and Gallery places are available exclusively for purchase one hour before the start of each concert. Tickets for both areas are £3.00 per person.

Arena places:
Look for the sign 'Arena Promenade Queue' at Door 2.

Gallery places:
Look for the sign 'Gallery Promenade Queue' at Door 10.

Special arrangements apply for the Last Night – please see opposite.

Guarantee a Proms place – buy a season ticket

Please note that all season ticket holders are able to join an express queue for entrance to the hall.

Whole Season tickets
Arena	£135.00
Gallery	£95.00

Covers all Proms concerts (including the Last Night)

Half Season tickets
Arena	£80.00
Gallery	£55.00

First Half: Proms 1–40
(18 July – 17 August)

Second Half: Proms 41–72
(18 August – 12 September)

And new this year – Quarter Season tickets

Quarter Season tickets
Arena	£45.00
Gallery	£32.00

First Quarter: Proms 1–20
(18 July – 3 August)

Second Quarter: Proms 21–40
(4–17 August)

Third Quarter: Proms 41–57
(18–31 August)

Fourth Quarter: Proms 58–72
(1–12 September)

Half and Quarter Season tickets do *not* include the Last Night. An allocation of tickets for the Last Night will, however, be specially reserved for those holding Half Season tickets. Please see opposite for further details.

Please provide two passport-sized photographs with all season ticket applications.

All season tickets guarantee admission until 10 minutes before each concert for which the ticket is valid.

At 10 minutes before each concert, all remaining queues will be given equal priority.

Please note that for the Junior Prom on 8 September season tickets will be valid for admission to the Gallery only. No Arena spaces are available.

Seats

Each purchaser buying tickets for at least six other concerts in the 1997 Proms season may apply for one ticket in the same price range for the Last Night.

For example, if you purchase one ticket in the Choir for six concerts, you are entitled to apply for one ticket in the Choir for the Last Night. If you purchase two tickets in the Stalls for six concerts, you are entitled to apply for two tickets in the Stalls for the Last Night.

However, each applicant is only allowed a maximum of two Last Night tickets.

For example, if you purchase five tickets in the Stalls for six concerts, you are entitled to apply for two tickets only in the Stalls for the Last Night.

If you book tickets for at least six concerts but in different seating areas, you will be allocated seats in the area of the majority of your bookings, unless otherwise directed by you that lower-priced tickets are required.

We regret that if the Last Night is sold out by the time your application is dealt with, no refunds for other tickets purchased will be payable.

Standing places

Prommers who have attended six or more concerts can purchase a ticket for the Last Night (*subject to availability*).

Apply at the Ticket Shop with six ticket stubs (all different concerts) and £3.00.

Whole Season tickets include admission to the Last Night.

An allocation of tickets for the Last Night will be reserved for those holding **Half Season** tickets. Simply present your Half Season ticket, together with £3.00, at the Ticket Shop after 23 July (First Half season) or 22 August (Second Half season).

Those holding **Quarter Season** tickets – for whichever Quarter – may also apply for tickets in person at the Ticket Shop after 23 July. However, no special allocation of Last Night tickets is held for Quarter Season ticket holders.

Premiere Nights

Concerts which appear with this symbol in the listings and on the booking form have tickets on offer at a saving of £3.00 from the normal price (*except* Circle restricted view) provided you book using the booking form in this Guide (pages 129–132).

Premiere Price

Stalls	£17.00
Loggia Boxes *(8 seats)*	£17.00
2nd Tier Boxes *(5 seats)*	£12.50
Choir	£9.50
Front Circle	£8.50
Rear Circle	£6.00

Normal prices

Stalls	£20.00
Loggia Boxes *(8 seats)*	£20.00
2nd Tier Boxes *(5 seats)*	£15.50
Choir	£12.50
Front Circle	£11.50
Rear Circle	£9.00

Remember to fill in the special Premiere Price when completing your booking form.

Sunday 20 July
John Adams Scratchband
UK premiere

Thursday 24 July
Korngold Violanta
London premiere

Tuesday 29 July
Sofia Gubaidulina
Viola Concerto
European premiere

Sunday 3 August
Giya Kancheli Symphony No. 3
UK premiere

Wednesday 20 August
Sibelius The Wood Nymph
London premiere

Tuesday 26 August
Elliott Carter Allegro scorrevole
European premiere

Same Day Savers

To gain even more from your visit to the Proms, we have produced a Same Day Saver to encourage you, on some days when more than one concert is taking place, to linger in the Hall and enjoy an extra concert.

Same Day Savers allow a £2.00 discount on some afternoon and Late Night Concerts, provided tickets for these are purchased at the same time as tickets for the main evening concert on the same day.

Same Day Savers are not available for Arena and Gallery.

Group Bookings

This year, for the first time, special discounts are available for groups of 10 or more. For further information, please call the Royal Albert Hall Ticket Shop on **0171 838 3108** and ask for Group Bookings.

How to Book

When to make your booking

Priority postal and fax bookings begin on **Wednesday 21 May**. Between 21 May and 16 June the *only way* that bookings can be made is by sending in the booking form on pages 129–132 of this Guide.

All postal or fax forms received before Wednesday 21 May will be dealt with as if they had arrived on that day.

Postal booking address is
**BBC Proms Ticket Shop,
Royal Albert Hall,
London SW7 2AP**

Fax booking number is
0171 225 0439

If you fax your booking, no postal confirmation is required.

Express orders

The following orders, sent by post or fax within the priority booking period, will go into an EXPRESS booking track:

- **Concerts in price codes B or C provided they also include at least one code A concert**

Those booking concerts in price codes B and C, but who do not wish also to book a concert in price code A, will have their orders dealt with once the express orders have been fulfilled, but before telephone and personal booking opens on 16 June.

- **Concerts in price codes A and/or D**

- **Season Tickets – whether Whole, Half or Quarter Seasons**

Telephone booking begins on **Monday 16 June**
Call **0171 589 8212**

Personal booking begins on **Monday 16 June**
Visit the Royal Albert Hall Ticket Shop at Door 7.

The box office is open daily from 9.00am to 9.00pm

RAH Events Line
For recorded ticket information you can call 0891 500 252 24 hours per day. Calls are charged at 45p per minute cheap rate, and 50p at all other times.

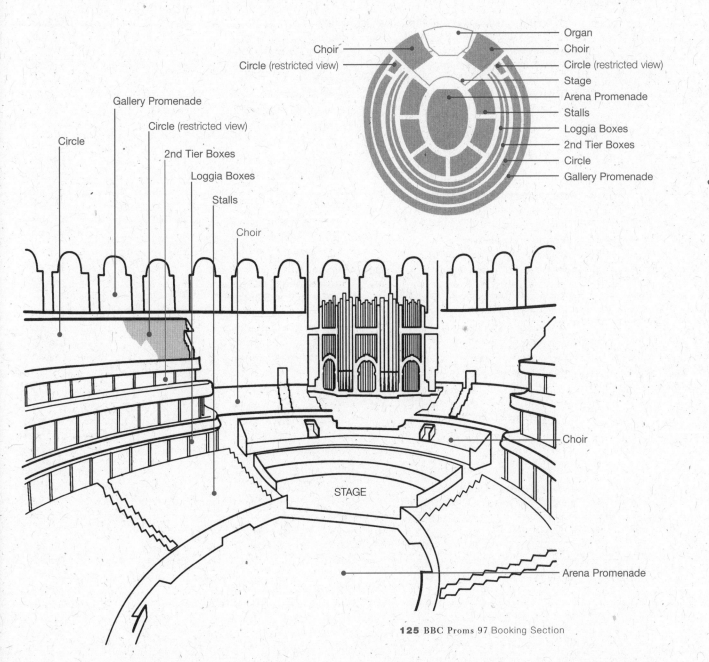

Choir
Circle (restricted view)

Organ
Choir
Circle (restricted view)
Stage
Arena Promenade
Stalls
Loggia Boxes
2nd Tier Boxes
Circle
Gallery Promenade

Gallery Promenade
Circle (restricted view)
2nd Tier Boxes
Loggia Boxes
Stalls
Choir
Circle

Choir

STAGE

Arena Promenade

Choose your seat

Price bands

Remember that each concert falls into one of five different price bands. Bands are colour coded for easy reference.

Privately owned seats
A high proportion of boxes, as well as 600 Stalls seats, are privately owned. Unless returned by owners, these seats are not available for sale.

Circle (formerly Balcony)
Prior to the 1996 Proms season, the Royal Albert Hall completed an extensive refurbishment of the Balcony, which it now renamed the Circle. The new seating offers increased leg-room, fewer restricted sightlines and a more comfortable environment. Catering facilities have also been upgraded, with the new West Circle Restaurant offering a salad bar and grill.

To reflect these improvements, the Circle has been segmented into different prices, Front Circle (the first three rows) and Rear Circle (rows 4 to 7).

Wheelchair spaces
Wheelchair spaces are available at the back of the stalls area (see plan on previous page) at the same price as nearby stalls seats. The price of the ticket includes a seat for a helper. See page 134 for booking details.

A
Stalls	£20.00
Loggia Boxes *(8 seats)*	£20.00
2nd Tier Boxes *(5 seats)*	£15.50
Choir	£12.50
Front Circle	£11.50
Rear Circle	£9.00
Circle *(restricted view)*	£5.00

B
Stalls	£25.00
Loggia Boxes *(8 seats)*	£25.00
2nd Tier Boxes *(5 seats)*	£20.00
Choir	£15.00
Front Circle	£13.00
Rear Circle	£10.00
Circle *(restricted view)*	£6.00

C
Stalls	£32.00
Loggia Boxes *(8 seats)*	£32.00
2nd Tier Boxes *(5 seats)*	£27.00
Choir	£20.00
Front Circle	£16.00
Rear Circle	£12.50
Circle *(restricted view)*	£8.00

D
Stalls	£8.00
Loggia Boxes *(8 seats)*	£8.00
2nd Tier Boxes *(5 seats)*	£8.00
Choir	£8.00
Front Circle	£8.00
Rear Circle	£8.00
Circle *(restricted view)*	N/A

E
Stalls	£65.00
Loggia Boxes *(8 seats)*	£65.00
2nd Tier Boxes *(5 seats)*	£65.00
Choir	£45.00
Front Circle	£45.00
Rear Circle	£40.00
Circle *(restricted view)*	£20.00

Fill in the number of tickets you require for each of your chosen concerts.

Be careful to write the number in the box under your chosen seating area.

Add up the amount spent on tickets at the end of each column (see example).

If the tickets you want are not available, lower-priced tickets for the same concert will be sent. Please tick the box on the booking form if this is NOT acceptable.

Tickets cannot be exchanged for other performances nor refunded except in the event of a cancelled performance. The BBC reserves the right to substitute artists and vary programmes if necessary.

Booking Queries

If you have any queries about how to fill in this booking form please call the Ticket Shop Helpline on 0171 589 8212 from 7 May.

Car Parking

£5.00 per evening. See page 133 for further details.

Booking form

Seating Area: please indicate number of seats required

Concert		Time	Price Code		Stalls	Loggia Boxes (8 seats)	2nd Tier Boxes (5 seats)	Choir	Front Circle	Rear Circle	Circle (restricted view)	Car Parking	Total (£)		Office Use
1	Friday 18 July	7.30	B											:	
2	Saturday 19 July	7.30	A											:	
3	Sunday 20 July	7.30	A	Premiere Night										:	
4	Monday 21 July	7.30	A											:	
5	Tuesday 22 July	7.30	A					2					25	: 00	
6	Wednesday 23 July	7.00	A	Same Day Saver				2					25	: 00	
7	Wednesday 23 July	10.00	D	Same Day Saver				2					12	: 00	
8	Thursday 24 July	7.30	A	Premiere Night										:	
9	Friday 25 July	7.30	A											:	
10	Saturday 26 July	7.30	A											:	
11	Sunday 27 July	7.30	A											:	
12	Monday 28 July	7.30	A											:	
13	Tuesday 29 July	7.30	A	Premiere Night										:	
14	Wednesday 30 July	7.30	A											:	
15	Thursday 31 July	7.00	A	Same Day Saver										:	
16	Thursday 31 July	10.00	D	Same Day Saver										:	
17	Friday 1 August	7.00	A											:	
18	Saturday 2 August	7.30	B											:	
71	Thursday 11 Sept	7.30	C											:	
72	Friday 12 Sept	7.30	C											:	
73	Saturday 13 Sept	7.30	E	The Last Night										:	
	Booking fee												1	: 50	
												Total	63	: 50	

Your notes

This page can be used to make any notes of Proms you may want to attend or that you have booked

Booking form

Seating Area: please indicate number of seats required

Concert		Time	Price Code		Stalls	Loggia Boxes (8 seats)	2nd Tier Boxes (5 seats)	Choir	Front Circle	Rear Circle	Circle (restricted view)	Car Parking	Total (£)	Office Use
1	Friday 18 July	7.30	B										:	
2	Saturday 19 July	7.30	A										:	
3	Sunday 20 July	7.30	A	● Premiere Night									:	
4	Monday 21 July	7.30	A										:	
5	Tuesday 22 July	7.30	A										:	
6	Wednesday 23 July	7.00	A	⤤ Same Day Saver									:	
7	Wednesday 23 July	10.00	D	⤤ Same Day Saver									:	
8	Thursday 24 July	7.30	A	● Premiere Night									:	
9	Friday 25 July	7.30	A										:	
10	Saturday 26 July	7.30	A										:	
11	Sunday 27 July	7.30	A										:	
12	Monday 28 July	7.30	A										:	
13	Tuesday 29 July	7.30	A	● Premiere Night									:	
14	Wednesday 30 July	7.30	A										:	
15	Thursday 31 July	7.00	A	⤤ Same Day Saver									:	
16	Thursday 31 July	10.00	D	⤤ Same Day Saver									:	
17	Friday 1 August	7.00	A										:	
18	Saturday 2 August	7.30	B										:	
19	Sunday 3 August	4.00	A										:	
20	Sunday 3 August	7.30	A	● Premiere Night									:	
21	Monday 4 August	7.30	A										:	
22	Tuesday 5 August	7.30	A										:	
23	Wednesday 6 August	7.30	B										:	
24	Thursday 7 August	7.30	A										:	
25	Friday 8 August	7.00	A	⤤ Same Day Saver									:	
26	Friday 8 August	10.00	D	⤤ Same Day Saver									:	
27	Saturday 9 August	7.30	A										:	
28	Sunday 10 August	3.00	A										:	
												Total carried over	:	

Booking form

Concert		Time	Price Code			Stalls	Loggia Boxes (8 seats)	2nd Tier Boxes (5 seats)	Choir	Front Circle	Rear Circle	Circle (restricted view)	Car Parking	Total (£)	Office Use
												Total carried over		⋮	
29	Sunday 10 August	7.30	C											⋮	
30	Monday 11 August	7.30	A											⋮	
31	Tuesday 12 August	7.00	A	🔁 Same Day Saver										⋮	
32	Tuesday 12 August	10.00	D	🔁 Same Day Saver										⋮	
33	Wednesday 13 August	7.30	A											⋮	
34	Thursday 14 August	7.30	B											⋮	
35	Friday 15 August	7.00	A	🔁 Same Day Saver										⋮	
36	Friday 15 August	10.00	D	🔁 Same Day Saver										⋮	
37	Saturday 16 August	7.00	A	🔁 Same Day Saver										⋮	
38	Saturday 16 August	10.00	D	🔁 Same Day Saver										⋮	
39	Sunday 17 August	4.00	D	🔁 Same Day Saver										⋮	
40	Sunday 17 August	8.00	B	🔁 Same Day Saver										⋮	
41	Monday 18 August	7.30	A											⋮	
42	Tuesday 19 August	7.00	A	🔁 Same Day Saver										⋮	
43	Tuesday 19 August	10.00	D	🔁 Same Day Saver										⋮	
44	Wednesday 20 August	7.30	A	● Premiere Night										⋮	
45	Thursday 21 August	7.30	A											⋮	
46	Friday 22 August	7.30	A											⋮	
47	Saturday 23 August	7.30	A											⋮	
48	Sunday 24 August	3.00	A	FULL PRICE FOR ADULTS / HALF PRICE FOR UNDER 14's*										⋮	
49	Sunday 24 August	7.30	A											⋮	
50	Monday 25 August	7.30	B											⋮	
51	Tuesday 26 August	7.30	A	● Premiere Night										⋮	
52	Wednesday 27 August	7.30	B											⋮	
53	Thursday 28 August	7.00	C	🔁 Same Day Saver										⋮	
54	Thursday 28 August	10.00	D	🔁 Same Day Saver										⋮	
55	Friday 29 August	7.30	A											⋮	
	*Not restricted view, Arena or Gallery											Total carried over		⋮	

Seating Area: please indicate number of seats required

Concert		Time	Price Code			Stalls	Loggia Boxes (8 seats)	2nd Tier Boxes (5 seats)	Choir	Front Circle	Rear Circle	Circle (restricted view)	Car Parking	Total (£)		Office Use
													Total carried over	:		
56	Saturday 30 August	7.30	A											:		
57	Sunday 31 August	7.30	A											:		
58	Monday 1 Sept	7.00	A											:		
59	Tuesday 2 Sept	7.30	B											:		
60	Wednesday 3 Sept	7.30	B											:		
61	Thursday 4 Sept	7.00	A	↗ Same Day Saver										:		
62	Thursday 4 Sept	10.00	D	↗ Same Day Saver										:		
63	Friday 5 Sept	7.30	A											:		
64	Saturday 6 Sept	7.30	A											:		
65	Sunday 7 Sept	7.30	A											:		
66	Monday 8 Sept	2.30		Junior Prom – Tickets are not available through the Royal Albert Hall Ticket Shop. For further information please phone 0171 765 5666												
67	Monday 8 Sept	7.30	A											:		
68	Tuesday 9 Sept	7.30	B											:		
69	Wednesday 10 Sept	7.00	A	↗ Same Day Saver										:		
70	Wednesday 10 Sept	10.00	D	↗ Same Day Saver										:		
71	Thursday 11 Sept	7.30	C											:		
72	Friday 12 Sept	7.30	C											:		
73	Saturday 13 Sept	7:30	E	The Last Night										:		
	Booking fee													1 : 50		
													Total	:		

Proms Chamber Music – Mondays at 1.00pm (all tickets £5.00: no booking fee)

Date	Number of tickets	Total (£)	Date	Number of tickets	Total (£)
21 July		:	18 August		:
28 July		:	25 August		:
4 August		:	1 September		:
11 August		:	8 September		:
Total carried over		:	Total		:

Now please turn over and fill in the payment details on the reverse

Season Tickets and Payment Details

Season Ticket	Dates	Arena	Gallery	No. of tickets Arena	Gallery
Whole Season	Friday 18 July – Saturday 13 September	£135.00	£95.00		
First Half	Friday 18 July – Sunday 17 August	£80.00	£55.00		
Second Half	Monday 18 August – Friday 12 September	£80.00	£55.00		
First Quarter	Friday 18 July – Sunday 3 August	£45.00	£32.00		
Second Quarter	Monday 4 August – Sunday 17 August	£45.00	£32.00		
Third Quarter	Monday 18 August – Sunday 31 August	£45.00	£32.00		
Fourth Quarter	Monday 1 September – Friday 12 September	£45.00	£32.00		
Booking Fee			£1.50		
			Total		

(BLOCK CAPITALS PLEASE) Name ....

Address ....

....Postcode...

Daytime Telephone Number ....Evening Telephone Number..

By credit card Please debit my Access/Visa/American Express/Mastercard account for: £............................

My card number is:

Expiry Date:

Signature...

Or by Cheque

☐ I enclose a cheque made payable to the Royal Albert Hall. Please leave cheques open, with an upper limit.

☐ Season Ticket photographs enclosed.

☐ Do not send lower-priced tickets.

☐ My ticket order qualifies as an Express Order.

☐ Order sent by fax. Please indicate the total number of pages sent ....

Please remember to enclose two passport-sized photographs with all season ticket applications.
Please note that a charge of £1.50 per booking will be added to cover postage and administration. When making your booking, you will automatically be sent a personal account number to link in with our computerised system. Please quote this number in all future transactions. Tickets will be delivered within 28 days. **Return your form to: BBC Proms Ticket Shop, Royal Albert Hall, London SW7 2AP**

Performance Time

Most concerts begin at 7.30pm, but please check individual concert dates or your ticket for accurate information. Doors open three-quarters of an hour before each concert (one hour before for Arena and Gallery Promenade areas). On days when there are two concerts, there may be a slight delay in the opening of doors for the second concert.

Late Arrivals

Latecomers will not be admitted into the Hall unless or until there is a suitable break in the music. There is a stereo relay in the foyer at Door 6.

Cloakroom facilities

Bags and coats may be left in the cloakroom at Door 4. Hand-luggage larger than a briefcase, folding chairs and food and drink are not allowed into the Hall.

Dining and Refreshments

Both the West Circle Restaurant (Door 8) and the East Circle Restaurant (Door 5) are open for meals two hours prior to each concert. Tables in the East Circle Restaurant can be booked in advance. Dining can also be found in the Prince Consort Restaurant, through Doors 13/14. Bars are located on every floor. For further details see page 137 or call 0171 589 8900.

Inside the Hall

There is no smoking inside the auditorium, and the use of cameras, tape-recorders and video cameras is strictly forbidden. Please do not bring mobile phones into the auditorium.

Bringing your Children to the Proms

Children are welcome at the Proms but in consideration of our audience and performers, children under the age of five are not allowed in the auditorium. The management reserves the right to refuse admission.

Programmes

Available at various points around the Hall.

Merchandise

A selection of BBC Proms merchandise will be on sale in the Foyer at Door 6 and at Door 8 in the Circle.

Broadcasting

All concerts are broadcast live on BBC Radio 3 and some will be shown on BBC Television. Please bear in mind the need for silence during the performance and show consideration for the musicians, fellow concert-goers and listeners at home by putting your hand over your mouth if you need to cough and by turning off your watch alarms.

Car Parking

A limited number of car park spaces are available at Imperial College (entrance in Prince Consort Road) for £5.00. Just tick the column on the booking form when applying for your tickets. Car parking is available from 6.00pm for evening concerts and from 2.00pm for weekend matinees.

At the Proms

Concert-goers with special needs

The Royal Albert Hall has up to 22 spaces for concert-goers in wheelchairs. Entrance is via Door 13/14. Phone the Ticket Shop on **0171 589 3203 ext. 2670** or apply using the booking form, marking one stalls seat by each concert of your choice, and adding the words 'wheelchair space'. Please note that concert-goers in wheelchairs can bring a helper free.

An infra-red sound enhancement system is available for the hard of hearing. Receivers may be obtained free of charge from the Information Desk at Door 6.

Unaccompanied visually impaired concert-goers wishing to promenade in the Arena or Gallery should phone the Front of House Manager on **0171 589 3203 ext. 2404** in advance.

Passenger lifts can be found off the ground floor corridor at Doors 2, 8 and 11.

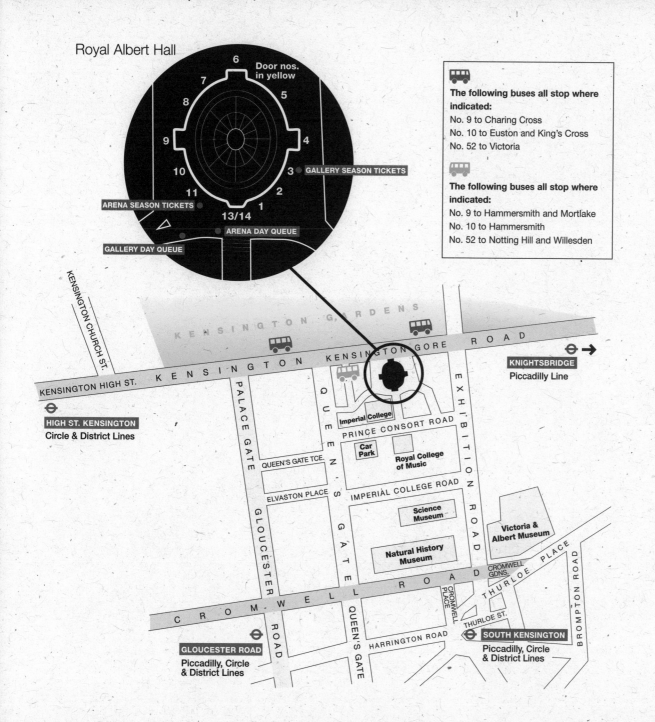

Royal Albert Hall

6
7
8
5
9
4
10
3 • GALLERY SEASON TICKETS
11
2
ARENA SEASON TICKETS •
1
13/14

Door nos. in yellow

• ARENA DAY QUEUE

GALLERY DAY QUEUE

The following buses all stop where indicated:
No. 9 to Charing Cross
No. 10 to Euston and King's Cross
No. 52 to Victoria

The following buses all stop where indicated:
No. 9 to Hammersmith and Mortlake
No. 10 to Hammersmith
No. 52 to Notting Hill and Willesden

KENSINGTON GARDENS

KENSINGTON CHURCH ST.

KENSINGTON HIGH ST.

KENSINGTON GORE ROAD

KNIGHTSBRIDGE
Piccadilly Line

HIGH ST. KENSINGTON
Circle & District Lines

Imperial College

PRINCE CONSORT ROAD

PALACE GATE

QUEEN'S GATE

EXHIBITION ROAD

Car Park

Royal College of Music

QUEEN'S GATE TCE.

ELVASTON PLACE

IMPERIAL COLLEGE ROAD

GLOUCESTER ROAD

Science Museum

Natural History Museum

Victoria & Albert Museum

CROMWELL GDNS.

THURLOE PLACE

BROMPTON ROAD

CROMWELL ROAD

CROMWELL PLACE

THURLOE ST.

GLOUCESTER ROAD
Piccadilly, Circle & District Lines

HARRINGTON ROAD

QUEEN'S GATE

SOUTH KENSINGTON
Piccadilly, Circle & District Lines

How to get there

encore!

BBC PROMS 97 in the PARK

Giant screen relay live from the Royal Albert Hall - Last Night of the Proms finale

Saturday 13th September. Hyde Park

BBC

Back by Popular demand, the Last Night of the Proms returns to Hyde Park. It's your chance to join in with the Albert Hall Promenaders at London's biggest musical party. To join the priority mailing list for details of the event please complete the tear-off slip below and send to: Proms in the Park, BBC Proms Ticket Shop, Royal Albert Hall, London SW7 2AP.

(BLOCK CAPITALS)

Name ....

Address ....

Telephone ....

The three restaurants and Champagne Bar are open 2 hours before each performance, allowing ample time for relaxed dining.

Eating and drinking
at the Royal Albert Hall

RESTAURANTS

The EAST CIRCLE RESTAURANT (formerly the Victoria Restaurant) offers a choice of a 2 or 3 course fixed price à la carte menu. New for 1997 is the Salads and Grills selection in the refurbished WEST CIRCLE RESTAURANT (formerly the Elgar Room), whilst the PRINCE CONSORT RESTAURANT on the Grand Tier is ideal for light meals and snacks. Food can be pre-ordered for the interval at all three restaurants.

BARS

There are bars on all floors serving alcoholic and non-alcoholic drinks, as well as a choice of sandwiches, confectionery and ice cream. Drinks can be pre-ordered for the interval at all bars.

CHAMPAGNE BAR

The Champagne Bar offers a variety of wines, spirits and beers as well as a range of vintage and non-vintage champagnes. Light food is available to complement your choice.

BOX HOSPITALITY

A range of food and drink can be pre-ordered for your box. Details of our Box Hospitality service are available by telephoning 0171 589 8900.

PRIVATE FUNCTIONS

The Royal Albert Hall boasts a number of elegant private rooms which provide unique venues for corporate or private functions.

TO MAKE A RESERVATION IN THE EAST CIRCLE RESTAURANT, OR FOR DETAILS OF THE BOX HOSPITALITY AND PRIVATE FUNCTION SERVICE, PLEASE CALL LETHEBY & CHRISTOPHER ON 0171 589 8900.

LETHEBY & CHRISTOPHER
CATERING MADE SPECIAL

PLEASE NOTE THAT ONLY FOOD AND DRINK PURCHASED AT
THE ROYAL ALBERT HALL MAY BE CONSUMED ON THE PREMISES.

Proms 97 – Pre-Prom Talks

Composers, conductors, directors and other experts introduce new and rare works at the Proms at informal Pre-Prom Talks. All talks take place in the Concert Hall of the Royal College of Music. Admission is free.

Sunday 20 July
John Adams &
Michael Gordon   (6.15pm)

Wednesday 23 July
Iannis Xenakis   (5.45pm)

Friday 25 July
Sir Peter Maxwell Davies (6.15pm)

Saturday 26 July
Jonathan Harvey   (6.15pm)

Sunday 27 July
Deborah Warner
on Joan of Arc   (6.15pm)

Tuesday 29 July
Sofia Gubaidulina   (6.15pm)

Thursday 31 July
David Sawer   (5.45pm)

Monday 4 August
Roger Reynolds   (6.15pm)

Monday 11 August
Magnus Lindberg   (6.15pm)

Tuesday 12 August
Pierre Boulez   (5.45pm)

Wednesday 13 August
George Benjamin   (6.15pm)

Sunday 17 August
The BBC Proms Lecture (6.00pm)

Philip Brett has written thought-provoking and sometimes controversial reappraisals of Britten's life and work. Here he assesses the process by which Britten became a central figure in our musical life. The lecture will be broadcast on Radio 3 as part of the Britten Weekend. Admission is free.

Monday 18 August
Edward McGuire   (6.30pm)

Wednesday 20 August
Osmo Vänskä on Sibelius (6.15pm)

Tuesday 26 August
Elliott Carter   (6.15pm)

Index of Artists

*First appearance at a BBC Henry Wood Promenade Concert. **Bold** figures refer to Prom numbers

A

John Abulafia director* **19**
John Adams conductor **3**
Thomas Adès piano* **32**
John Mark Ainsley tenor **23**
Evgeny Akimov tenor* **34**
Thomas Allen baritone **45**
Stig Andersen tenor* **65**
Jon Runar Arason tenor* **67**
Hans Aschenbach tenor* **8**
David Atherton conductor **64**
Emanuel Ax piano **68**

B

Martin Baker organ* **39**
Patricia Bardon mezzo-soprano **42**
Yuri Bashmet viola **13**
Joshua Bell violin **49**
Jiří Bělohlávek conductor **17, 25**
Nathan Berg bass-baritone* **17**
Susan Bickley mezzo-soprano **2**
Hans Peter Blochwitz tenor **40**
Olga Borodina mezzo-soprano **72**
Ian Bostridge tenor **37**
Pierre Boulez conductor **31**
Martyn Brabbins conductor **24**
Alfred Brendel piano **53**
Aline Brewer harp* **39**
Iona Brown conductor **37**
Timothy Brown horn **37**
Andrew Burden tenor* **38**

C

Janice Cairns soprano **8**
Nicolas Cavallier bass **19**
Riccardo Chailly conductor **59, 60**
Michael Chance counter-tenor **58**
Susan Chilcott soprano **23**
Paul Charles Clarke tenor **42**
Natalie Clein cello* **48**
Stephen Cleobury conductor **36**

Sarah Connolly mezzo-soprano **11**
Alice Coote mezzo-soprano* **11**
Ronald Corp conductor **66**
Michèle Crider soprano* **72**

D

Inger Dam-Jensen soprano* **24**
Nicholas Daniel oboe **39**
Paul Daniel conductor **8**
John Dankworth conductor* **55**
Neal Davies bass* **42**
Sir Peter Maxwell Davies conductor **9**
Andrew Davis conductor
6, 33, 40, 50, 73
Sir Colin Davis conductor **27**
Michelle DeYoung mezzo-soprano* **25**
Larissa Diadkova mezzo-soprano* **34**
Stella Doufexis mezzo-soprano* **17**

E

Mark Elder conductor **42**
Ansor Erkomaishvili conductor* **26**
Anne Evans soprano **73**

F

Elena Ferrari soprano* **8**
Bernarda Fink mezzo-soprano* **29**
Gerald Finley bass **23**
Iván Fischer conductor **35**
Claus Peter Flor conductor **69**

G

John Eliot Gardiner conductor **29**
Daniele Gatti conductor **46**
Valery Gergiev conductor **34**
Gordon Gietz tenor* **29**
Evelyn Glennie percussion **10**
John Graham-Hall tenor **11**

H

Alison Hagley soprano **17**

Bernard Haitink conductor **1, 68**
Ken Hakii viola* **59**
Simon Halsey musical director* **38**
Thomas Hampson baritone* **40, 42**
Håkan Hardenberger trumpet **51**
Quentin Hayes baritone* **38**
Evelyn Herlitzius soprano* **63**
Richard Hickox conductor **10**
Rolf Hind piano **32**
Bo Holten conductor **54**
Godfried Hoogeveen cello* **59**
Stephen Hough piano **15**
Jason Howard baritone **18**
Judith Howarth soprano **2, 64**
Eileen Hulse soprano **11**

I

Steven Isserlis cello **5**
Ilya Itin piano* **47**

J

David James counter-tenor **20**
Neeme Järvi conductor **65, 67**
Ronnie Johansen bass* **67**
Anthony Rolfe Johnson tenor **14, 58, 67**
Charles Johnston baritone* **38**
Leila Josefowicz violin* **52**
Rosemary Joshua soprano **18**
Chantal Juillet violin* **65**

K

Liane Keegan mezzo-soprano* **8**
Evgeny Kissin piano **28**
Oliver Knussen conductor **51**
Ton Koopman conductor* **4**
Stephen Kovacevich piano **9**
Yakov Kreizberg conductor **22**
Hermann Kretzschmar organ* **3**
Solveig Kringelborn soprano **69**

L

Cleo Laine singer **55**
Lisa Larsson soprano* **2**
Alexander Lazarev conductor **20**
John Lill piano **6**
Tasmin Little violin **20**
Andrew Litton conductor **49**
Jeffrey Lloyd-Roberts tenor* **19**
Frank Lopardo tenor* **72**
Louis Lortie piano **64**
Nigel Lowery director* **8**
John Lubbock conductor **32**

M

Paul McCreesh conductor* **63**
Jamie MacDougall tenor* **2, 18**
Nicholas McGegan conductor* **2**
Joanna MacGregor piano **7**
Sir Charles Mackerras conductor **45, 58**
Marie McLaughlin soprano **19**
Elisabeth von Magnus alto* **4**
Anne Manson conductor* **19**
Sir Neville Marriner conductor **52, 53**
Wayne Marshall organ & piano **73**
Malcolm Martineau piano* **46**
Hillevi Martinpelto soprano **2**
Annick Massis soprano* **50**
Peter Mattei baritone* **69**
Karita Mattila soprano **1**
Donald Maxwell baritone **18**
Waltraud Meier mezzo-soprano* **14**
Klaus Mertens bass* **4**
Paul Meyer clarinet* **12**
Anthony Michaels-Moore baritone **1**
Alastair Miles bass **58**
Diana Montague mezzo-soprano **50**
Viktoria Mullova violin **33**

N

Kent Nagano conductor **13**

Index of Works

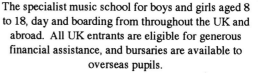
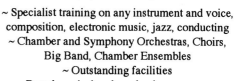

Index of Advertisers

8 **Rick Stein**
Mahler: Symphony No. 1
BBC Philharmonic
Jiří Bělohlávek (conductor)
Prom 21

3 **Amanda Redman**
Barber: Adagio for Strings
BBC Scottish Symphony Orchestra
Stewart Robertson (conductor)
Prom 32

4 **John Bird**
Brahms:
Symphony No. 2
BBC Philharmonic
Sir Charles Mackerras (conductor)
Prom 35

1 **Desmond Lynam**

Parry orch. Elgar: Jerusalem
BBC Symphony Orchestra
Andrew Davis (conductor)
Prom 73

John Adams:
Short Ride in a Fast Machine
BBC National Orchestra of Wales
Mark Elder (conductor)
Prom 73

Gilbert & Sullivan:
The Gondoliers
D'Oyly Carte Opera Orchestra
John Pryce-Jones (conductor)
Courtesy of TER Classics
Prom 18

Georgian Folk Song
Rustavi Choir
Ansor Erkomaishvili (conductor)
Prom 26

Schubert: String Quintet
Endellion Quartet
Robert Cohen (cello)
Proms Chamber Music
21 July

2 **Tony Robinson**
Bach: Brandenburg
Concerto No. 4
Amsterdam Baroque Orchestra
Ton Koopman (conductor)
Ⓟ 1985 Erato Classics SNC
Paris, France – complete
recording currently available on
Erato 0630-16164-2
Prom 4

7 **Simon Russell Beale**
Sibelius: Symphony No. 2
BBC Scottish Symphony Orchestra
Osmo Vänskä (conductor)
Prom 15

5 **Tim Henman**
Mozart: Clarinet Concerto
BBC National Orchestra
of Wales
Antony Pay (clarinet)
Prom 12

6 **Germaine Greer**
Britten: Rejoice in the Lamb
BBC Singers
Kevin Bowyer (organ)
Stephen Cleobury (conductor)
Prom 39

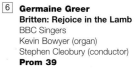